'Love extends beyond the bounds of family to all human beings and is changed into vivifying, creative, transmuting power.'

— Rudolph Steiner

Shazzie

First Edition: 11th November 2008: Blue Resonant Hand (Knows Accomplishment).

Edited by David Smith.

Book design by Mike Smith and design management by David Smith, sheepshank.org.

Cover design by Shakiba Mohseni, cover photography by Shazzie, cover artwork by Philip Shadbolt of Kundalini Arts, Brighton, kundaliniarts.co.uk.

Photography by Shazzie.

Additional recipes, research and copy by Adam Pinkerfield.

ISBN-10: 0-9543977-3-8
ISBN-13: 978-0-9543977-3-9

Printing
Printed in The United Kingdom of Great Britain by:
Rawcreation Ltd (rawcreation.com)
9/10 Morton Peto Estate (off Morton Peto Road), Great Yarmouth, Norfolk, NR31 0LT, UK

Disclaimer
This book is sold for information purposes only. Neither the author nor the publisher will be held accountable for the use or misuse of the information contained in this book. This book is not intended as medical advice, because the author and publisher are not medical doctors and do not recommend the use of medicines to achieve ecstatic bliss or to alleviate health challenges.

Because there is always some risk involved, the author, publisher and/or distributors of this book are not responsible for any adverse effects or consequences resulting from the use of any recipes, suggestions or procedures described hereafter.

Thank you

I've been writing this book since Evie's been eating food, and many people have supported and loved us both over that time. Having a mother-brain I've probably forgotten some of you – but only on paper, never in my heart.

Mum and Dad. As ever – so full of love and support, laughs and more laughs, reality, honesty, directness, warmth, connectedness, cuppoteas and never ending hugs. Wow. We picked such a great family!

Evie's Daddy, "Daddy Matt". Thanks for respecting our child's diet. Clearly she forgot to look in your kitchen cupboards when she was choosing us as parents, before she became a real person. Stagg Chili, Matt... Goodness.

Evie's fairy parents, Jennie, David Smith, Jane and Wayne. The placenta's still there. Everyone's still talking about your poem, David: "putting down toys, taking up boys".

Evie's Gran, Chris. You just know exactly what to say and do. Your love and extra pair of hands continue to be treasured over the years. The stickers you bring each week continue to decorate my house.

Kate Magic and boys. You're the bestest friend anyone could have. You eat the same (but less!), we have the same sense of humour, we have raw kiddies who play together, and most importantly, you understand the need to rewrite the future history of womankind. This is the Frilly Knickers Revolution, babe.

Rochelle Von Rockstar. Thank you for the music, the two-tone hair, the Reiki and the copious chatchups. You're a rock star superstar and Evie loves it when your songs come on my MacBoy. "It's Shell!" she says.

Yolie. Evie loved you from the moment you bought her those flip flops.

Ellie. Crystally rescuing one.

Jessie, Finlay and Baby Audrey. I hope you enjoyed tasting these creations.

Jatinder, Derek, Mohan, Priya, Ramen. I love you, my wonderful raw extended family.

Dale. Grateful smiles for your herbal nerdiness. Now get your own TV show!

Best shaman ever, **Sean**. Thank you for your astral travelling and allowing me to greet Xochipili.

Karla. Thank you for proof reading, and being too grammatically correct.

Scallywags Day Nursery in Westwick. Thank you for accommodating our requirements and showing us love.

A special dose of love to **Gillian McKeith** for your continual bigging up of real food in the UK and beyond. Ditto to **Jamie Oliver** here too, even though I don't know you (yet).

Ecstatic love to **Binnie Dansby** for revolutionising the attitudes of birthing in our culture.

Gracias to **Jock Doubleday** for being a knight in shining armour, highlighting the issues around childhood vaccines in a unique and exciting way.

Super thanks to **Philip Shadbolt** and **Bob** of kundaliniarts.co.uk for the beautiful art that follows me in my life. It's all too beautiful.

Big up to **Tish of Loveland**, who continually provides me with insights that go beyond anything I've ever known. Also, for the experiential input into this book. You are a treasure chest of information.

To all those raw families who are lighting the way, especially **Holly** with **Lizzy** and **Bertie**, **The Boutenkos** and **Rawqween ShakayaBreeze**.

And finally, big love to the usual suspects: **Veronika, Ruth, Joe, David Wolfe, Lakshmi Love God, Becky, James W, Dark Sunblade, Lisa Currants, Mrs Lisa Renny, Twinkel, Steph & Mike, Pippa, Cary, Arun, Debs, Mary Toscano, Daniela Vanilla, Aaron & Daddy Chris, Jonny, Claudia the onside journo, Helen of Helen's Kitchen, Jesus, Buddha, God, Goddess, The Universe, You.**

Dedications to Adam and Evie

To Evie

Not many children have a book written about the food they eat. Anyone would think you were a Leo and enjoyed basking in the limelight.

To Admmm

On 11th September 2008, my Personal Jesus Admmm flew high into the sky, no longer needing his earthly body. He still touches everyone so deeply as the memories of his light and love shine bright.

Admmm, a week before you got your wings you asked me to dedicate a book to you. I'm sure part of you knew that you were going away, far away. I miss you, Mr Ecstasist. I miss the whole bonkers unlimited you so much.

Thank you for helping me to write this book. You created lots of beautiful recipes, you did the science bit when the science bit was doing my head in, and you fine-tuned my words without losing their Shazzieness. I treasure all of your input.

There is no beginning and there is no end. You filled your 29 earthly years with love, life, liberty and divinity. My gratitude for your presence is infinite. Every depth and every high will stay in my heart for eternity. Thank you for restoring me to my original condition of being a fully functioning goddess, and seeing beyond the mamachine. I love you.

You were the liberator, now you're fully liberated
You were the ecstasist, now you're in eternal ecstasy
You were the lover, now you're pure love

Revel In Paradise, my infimate beautiful boy.

contents

Thank you . . . iii
Dedications to Adam and Evie . . . v
Contents . . . vi
Foreword by Jock Doubleday . . . x
Introduction . . . xiii

Eating naturally . . . 1

What is the raw food diet? . . . 6
Do I have to go all-raw, and all-vegan? . . . 20
How to start a child on raw food . . . 21
Starting a baby on raw foods . . . 24
The big differences . . . 26
Further information . . . 32

Nutrition and your child's future . . . 33

Basic nutritional requirements . . . 35
Why supplement? . . . 36
The ones to watch . . . 37
- Vitamin D . . . 37
- Vitamin B12 . . . 40
- Vitamin K1 and K2 . . . 41
- DHA and EPA . . . 44
- Iron . . . 46
- Calcium . . . 50
- Choline . . . 53

Further information . . . 54

Breastfeeding . . . 55

Reasons to be milky . . . 56
Detoxing before pregnancy and while breastfeeding . . . 57
Nature's first starter . . . 59
Nature's first food . . . 60
Nutritionally perfect . . . 61
Ooh, the pain . . . 61
What's natural? . . . 62
Milk is species-specific . . . 62
Full-term breastfeeding . . . 63
Poooooh! . . . 65
Not sleeping through the night . . . 65
Wet nursing and breastfeeding alternatives . . 66
Achieving the impossible — milk men . . . 67
Let it all flow . . . 68
After breastmilk . . . 68
Further information . . . 68

Natural parenting . . . 69

Ecstatic birthing . . . 70
Vaccinations . . . 71
Evie's first aid kit . . . 73
Co-sleeping . . . 77
Babywearing . . . 78
Conscious communication . . . 79
Free-range children . . . 81
Further information . . . 82

All about Evie . . . 83

Something in the oven . . . 85
A natural birth? . . . 86
The birthing . . . 87
Our first hours . . . 89
Our first months . . . 91
Such a life change . . . 91
Seeing the light . . . 92
All by ourselves . . . 92
Evie's first food . . . 93
Our sanctuary . . . 94
A natural child . . . 95
Child care . . . 95
Well-meaning strangers . . . 96
Christmas with a one-year-old . . . 96
A new reality . . . 97
Appreciating my miracle . . . 99
A blissing in disguise . . . 100
She's a big girl now . . . 101
My breastfeeding career . . . 102
Veggan? . . . 103
Admmm's magic . . . 104
The beginning . . . 106

Alchemy tools . . . 107

Alchemical ingredients . . . 109
Transatlantic translations . . . 114

Recipes

First foods: 6-12 months 115

Tropical fruit with breastmilk 116
Butternut mash 116
Sweet potato cake 116
Baby green juice 117
Spiralling out of the car seat 117
Lettuce pray 117
Apricot crumble 117
Maca'd up 118
Carob delight 118
Cream 118
Melon dramatic 118
Crystalmole with crudités 118
Durian 119
Crystal tips 119
Plum pudding 119
Raspberry pudding 119
Zebras 120
Coconut water 120
Nightea-night 120
Tummy troubles 120

Especially for breakfast 121

Bungalow cheeze 122
Nectarine sporridge 122
Holly's strawberry crumble 123
Quick mushrooms 124
Cucumber baguette 124
Breakfast bar 125
Buckwheat cereal 126
Buckwheaties 126
Breakfast for friends 127
Butternut tortilla 127
I'd rather have a bowl of cacao drops 128
Muffins w' stuffin 129
In a jam 130
Salbioca 130
Joe's faked ecstatic beans 131
Kerfuddled 'eggs' in tomato boats 132
Rascherry dip with fruit 133
Solstice morning sunshine sparkles 134

Soups 135

Brian can soup 136
Monster slime 136
Cucumber soup 137
Leek and sweet potato soup 137
Right said med 138
Red gazpacho soup 138
Green gazpacho soup 139
Mild creamy butternut curried soup 139
Give peas a chance 140
Spinach and parsley soup 140
Salba mantra soup 141
Asparagus and celery soup 142
Carrot and coriander soup 142
Tigger's vegetable soup 143
Steiner soup 143
Cabbage and apple soup 144
Thai coconut soup 144

Savoury main dishes 145

Deep down goji loaf 146
Creamy mushroom and sweetcorn pie 147
Sweet fragrant veg in da mix 148
Greenpeace 148
Okra casserole 149
Smorgasboard 149
Vegetable maki 151
Vegetable Sushi Maki Roll 151
Parsnip (or cauliflower), Sesame White Rice 151
Wasabi Aioli 151
SAF rice, shiitake, shiso, sweet pepper and wasabi aioli 151
Hemp croquettes 152
Pesto stuffed tomatoes 153
Nessie swims in her lake 154
Sage and onion sosages 155
Stir crazy 156
Deep sea patties 156
Tagliatelle devoted to you 157
Strawberry and hemp burritos 158
Comforting vegetable casserole 158
Russell Brand's hair fell on my plate 159

Golden nuggets 160
Crocodile's cauliflower crock.............161
Barbapapa's got a face full............ 162
Spacado 162
Cream of asparagus pies 163
Sprouted quinoa tabouleh............. 164
Seed and mushroom loaf............... 165
MushNuggets 166
Comforting miso casserole............. 167
Roastly veg 168

Salads.................169

Winter beetroot salad 170
Great curly carrots.....................171
Take a leek 171
Kale on Sunday 172
Squish............................ 173
Filling winter salad 174
Ensalada Mexicana 175
Princess Popple's salad 176
Cornutopia.......................... 176
There's something about celery slaw...... 177
Ecstatically yours 178

Savoury snacks and sides.................179

Nori batty 180
Nori roses 180
Cucumber canapés 181
Parsley parcels 181
Veggie chips......................... 182
Crisps 183
Kate's crackers 184
Crackers Indian style................. 185
Big potatno cake 186
Sandwich bread 187
Carrot wraps......................... 188
Not Kate's tomato crisps 189
Spicy fruit chutney 189
Christmas veggies.................... 190
Breadsticks 190
Med bread 191
Salba bread 192
Seaseeds........................... 193
Dinosaur caviar....................... 194
Olive and sundried tomato focaccia 195
Hard Cheeze......................... 196

Dips, dressings, sauces and spreads..............197

My mate 198
Cranberry sauce 198
Olive and hemp paté.................. 199
Heaven is a half piped cheezy cucumber... 200
Rochelle's rockstar cheeze 201
Deeply dippy 201
Smooth almond dressing............... 202
Sweet banana dressing 202
Hempesto 203
Shakti saucy......................... 203
Cottage squeeze...................... 204
Sauces for courses 205
Hempshine dip 206
Salbamole 206
Hummous cheeze 207
Evie can't believe it's not goat's cheese paté 208
Creamy curry dressing................. 209
Summer salsa........................ 210

Sweet things 211

Spoilt for chocolate cake............. 212
Shoelaces 213
Evie's Oompa Loompa cake 214
Sweet omega pudding.................. 215
Purple corn and fig crunchy buns 215
Choccie brownies 216
Love biscuits 217
Mango pudding 218
Goji pudding 218
Sunshiney day 219
Eclipse............................. 219
Mix of munch 219
Mexicoco 220
Clever mummy sorbet 220
Admmm's apple pie.................... 221
Ecstacake............................ 222
Gloopy chocolate dip 222
Bloopy chocolate dip 222
Soft chocolate fudge icing 223
Pancakes for any Tuesday because they're all special........................... 224
Lemon syrup 225
Dried pear with mulled goji salsa 225
Layers of love......................... 226

I scream for more 227
Omega dreamy cream 228
Mount morada 228
Flowery apricot fudge 229
I'm dreaming of a white chocolate 230
Grandma gives good lolly 230
Christine's orchid chocolate 231
Golden brown texture like sun 232
Gojiranium studge. 233
Purple corn and apricot crumbly chocolate . 234
Home torte. 235
Halloween howlers 236

Smoothies, juices, teas and other drinks. 237

Incredibly edible chocolate smoovie 238
Psychic kale smoothie. 238
Auntie Wee Wee 239
Pink milk. 239
Simply hemp mylk 240
Omega mylk. 240
Helen's kitchen 241
Mini Doxtor's juice 242
By the seaside smoothie 243
The Princess's sunshine smoothie. 243
Blade. 244
Go juice. 245
Goan, Goan, Gone. 245
A big fat Collins 246
I'm NOT tired! tea 247
Invincibili-tea 247

Bibliography 249

Foreword by Jock Doubleday

August 2008

In the beginning was nature. And nature said, "Let life spring from rock and water," and life sprang from rock and water in forms diverse and beautiful. And the forms of life knew boundaries of heat and cold beyond which they could not survive. And they lived within these boundaries or died beyond them...

All plant enzymes are destroyed at 50 degrees Celsius (122 degrees Fahrenheit). Many plant enzymes begin to denature (unravel, break apart) at lower temperatures.

The very concept, denature, is distasteful to the tastebuds of the brain. Is not nature primary, fundamental, the beginning and the end? What sort of species allows its food to become denatured before consuming it?

We look into the mirror at Homo agni, Fire Animal. The Fire Animal cooks and cooks and cooks again. Nothing escapes the infernal fire. "If it's not hot, it's not a meal".

We are told we must cook corn (the sweetest food on the planet before it's destroyed by heat), beets (if you have not tasted a raw beet, you have not lived), peas, even nuts. You'd have to be.

In every cooked meal, nature is denatured, flora deflowered, ancient bonds broken. This is truly regrettable, because nondestroyed plant enzymes spectacularly aid the human body in the digestive process.

What is the solution?

If you live near Shazzie, head over to her house. Her cupboards are the talk of the town. She expertly uses nature's flavorful blessings to keep herself and her daughter Evie amused, surprised, and satisfied, day after day, week after week, season after season.

If Shazzie's place is too far, you might walk out into your own garden, take a deep breath, or several, and when the breeze has brought you to yourself, let your knowing hands spread their fingers and choose a living meal from nature's kaleidoscopic offering, her phenomenal bounty.

No rush. This store never closes.

Nature, voiceless, cannot speak on the persistent folly of Homo agni. She can only continue, season after season, to create living gardens whose vibrant colors shout health in the same way that Hubble telescope photos of spiral galaxies shout order, and the deep expanses in a newborn's eyes whisper wisdom.

Nature gives us her gifts again and again and awaits our understanding. Those who wander Gaia's Garden are given the choice to accept her gifts without mediation or bathe them first in fire. Who would wander many years in health lets fire be.

Evie's Kitchen: Raising an ecstatic child offers an abundance of recipes for raw food, "recipes to love your child to life". But Evie's Kitchen is much more than a recipe book. It is a book that gives voice to nature's wisdom on a wide range of subjects, including natural birthing (ecstatic birthing), breastfeeding (ecstatic feeding), attachment parenting (ecstatic parenting), co-sleeping (you get the idea), natural immunity, natural detox, natural first aid, even the de-institutionalization of education. Yes, it's true, and we've always known it: schools are institutional daycare.

The physical and mental – need we mention emotional? – health of children in the Western world is at an abysmal low. It is a radical vision that lifts the veil of myth and sees children for what they are: natural beings struggling to survive a cultural world.

Evie's Kitchen encourages each of us to see Gaia for what it truly is: a garden, a teacher, a mother, a father – if only we will allow it to be.

Jock Doubleday, Ojai, California, USA

Author of *Spontaneous Creation: 101 Reasons Not to Have Your Baby in a Hospital*

introduction

I receive countless emails from women with young families. “What should I feed my baby when weaning?” or “How do I convert my child’s diet to raw?” or “Can I detox on raw food while pregnant?” or “What do you feed Evie, like, *every day*?”

Evie is my angel personified. She came to me as an entity the night I met her father. She came to me as a baby ten months later. She obviously wanted to be here, and fast! Why she wanted me to be her mother, when I’d escaped motherhood for 35 years before, I didn’t know. Why would she want to be so *different* to everyone else around her? What did I need to learn, what did I need to teach?

I’d been a vegan all my adult life. How was I going to raise my child in this world as a vegan? I’d been a raw foodist since 2000. Could I bring Evie up raw? Is it socially criminal to attempt this? Would we be outcasts? Would we create a community? Would we cause a revolution? What about the nutrition? Would she become deficient? I hadn’t – I’d become stronger and happier and healthier on a raw diet – but what about a toddler? What exactly do they need to thrive, to glow? As most dieticians gave us some very dubious advice, I wondered: do they lie or are they actually ignorant about real nutrition?

Thankfully the questions subsided as my left brain shut down during my pregnancy and new mother months. My intuitive right brain kicked in and all the answers came – eventually. What followed in the next few years felt as natural to me as I could have hoped for. And yes, Evie is thriving and glowing. As I write this, she is four years of age. Her raw food journey has taken some interesting twists and turns, and we’ve both learned so much. Evie was breastfed for four years. She’s one of the most sociable, well-adjusted, happy and content children I’ve ever met. She’s a true centre-stage Leo, too.

My hope for Evie to have a healthy, happy life is unfolding beautifully every day. Now I can finally document the answers I’ve found to assist you in your quest for an ecstatic child.

I hope that one day all children are raised with an abundance of raw and natural food. It’s the best decision I ever made for Evie. I hope this book inspires you to raise your children ecstatically. They all deserve it.

With love

Shazzie

Ecstatic Being : Visionary In Paradise : Author : Artist : Mother : Loveworker
www.shazzie.com
www.detoxyourworld.com

Eating naturally

In the western world we are blessed with abundance beyond the wildest dreams of our forefathers. No culture before has had the choice of living in such decadent luxury as ours. I would love to see us all begin to fully love ourselves, and be grateful for our privileged lifestyle.

Currently around half of the western world's population is overweight. Diseases such as diabetes, cancer, heart attack, arthritis, fibromyalgia and more are reaching epidemic proportions. Yet these are just symptoms of modern day living. Before fast food, intensive farming methods, crop spraying, genetically modified foods and cooking, our ancestors thrived on the raw food diet. Life wasn't as cosy for these people, but they were lean, healthy, connected and sane.

Compare the lifestyle of our ancestors with the insane culture we are part of today. Animals are reared for food without natural light, fed antibiotics daily and don't have enough room to walk or run. They queue up at the slaughterhouse knowing they're going to die, with masses of adrenaline circulating around their bodies. That adrenaline stays in the meat. People then eat the meat (and other animal parts) after they've been coated in batter that contains artificial chemicals and have been deep fried in metal pans full of three-week old oil. Why are we shocked when our loved ones go insane?

People can only thrive on the food they're meant to eat. We were never meant to eat most of the food that you see on stupormarket shelves. The only way to fix the fundamental issues in our society is to change what we are made of. To rebuild our world we must start by rebuilding ourselves. Everything else will then follow with no effort at all. You are what you eat, so if you eat food grown with love, made with love and eaten with love, you become love. Food grown and raised with fear creates fear in the person eating it. Intensively raised animals make for intensively raised people. You can see it when you look at people, once you tune in. Wild and strong food makes for wild and strong children. Wouldn't you just love your child to be wild, strong and free?

Children don't deserve to be poisoned at every mealtime by food their bodies don't recognise. Children deserve to have access to real food at all times. It's important that all children and their parents understand which foods cause them harm and which ones love them to life. As long as we leave the decision-making up to institutions such as schools and hospitals, our children will not gain optimal health and they won't be as smart and happy as they could be. Mothers and fathers: please reclaim the responsibility for your children's health, now.

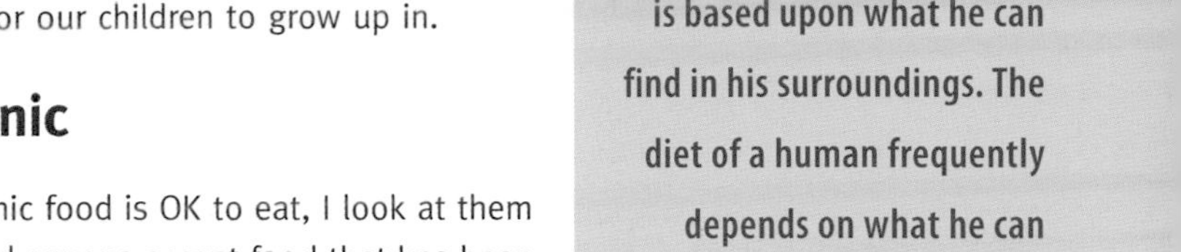

Let's all start the sane food revolution. Let's all say yes to raw, organic, home-grown, wild, ocean-grown, reiki'd up love food. Let's recreate a sane, beautiful and loving world for our children to grow up in.

The natural diet of an animal is based upon what he can find in his surroundings. The diet of a human frequently depends on what he can find in the stupormarket or on the restaurant menu. Natural animals will go to great lengths to get the meal their body is craving. Many humans seem to go to great lengths to avoid it.

Don't panic, it's organic

When people argue that non-organic food is OK to eat, I look at them with vague amusement. Why would anyone accept food that has been so messed about with? Can they really deny that the accumulation of thousands of toxins in our bodies creates havoc in the end? Why do they assume we can assimilate these toxins with no side-effects, when so many of them are new to us? Don't they see that people are unhealthier with these chemicals present in our lives, than before when they didn't exist? Do they never think "the whole is greater than the sum of its parts", therefore mixing a cocktail of chemicals and ingesting it with every meal may cause untold damage? I would never take that risk, for Evie or me.

A four-year £12m study funded by the EU has shown that organic foods do have more nutritional value than foods farmed using non-organic methods. The Quality Low Input Food Project, which took place on an English farm, grew both conventional and organic produce. The organic fruit and vegetables in the study contained up to 40 per cent more antioxidants than the conventionally farmed goods. The organic carrots contained more vitamin C than the non-organic carrots, and the organic spinach, lettuces and cabbages were higher in minerals. For more information on the world's largest study on organic food visit: www.qlif.org.

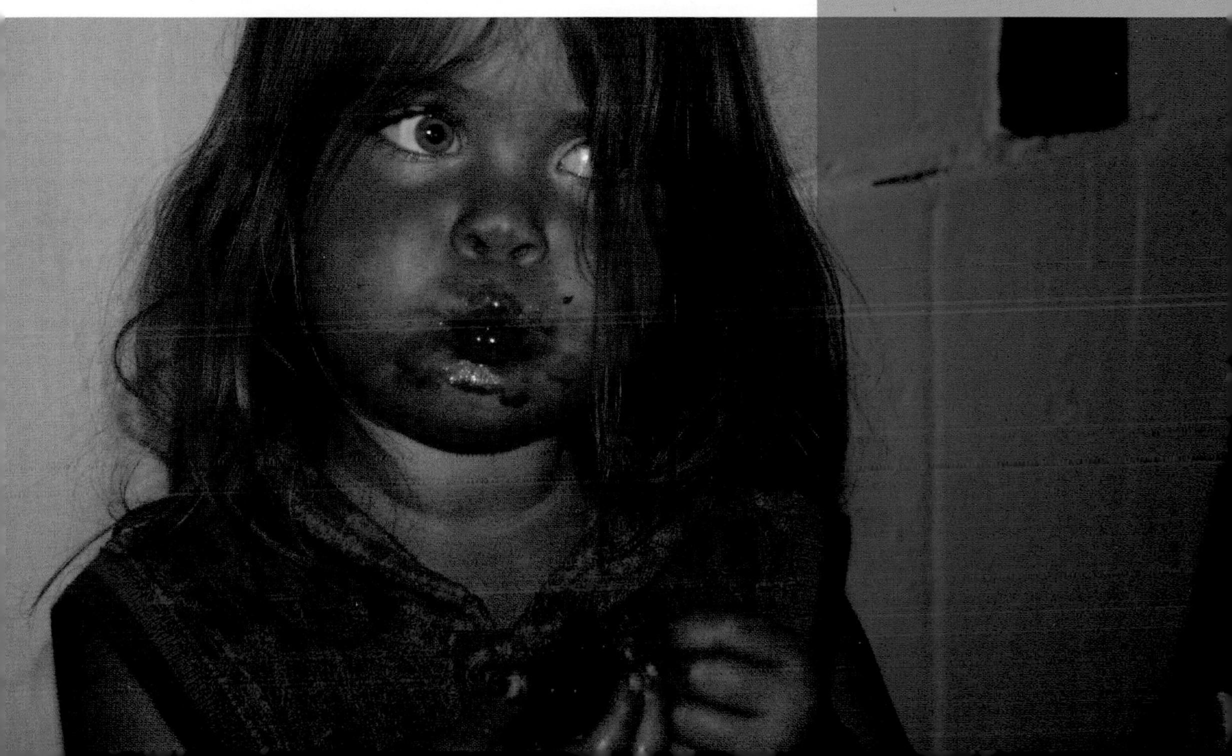

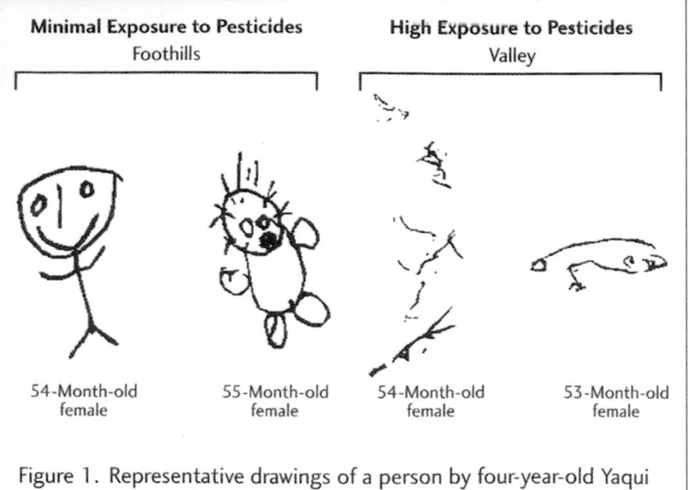

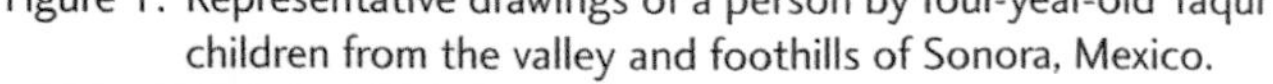
Figure 1. Representative drawings of a person by four-year-old Yaqui children from the valley and foothills of Sonora, Mexico.

Dr Gabriel Cousens is vastly experienced in raw food nutrition and therapy. He runs The Tree Of Life (retreat centre) in Arizona, USA and has written countless books. One book, *Rainbow Green Live Food Cuisine*, relates a study "An Anthropological Approach to the Evaluation of Preschool Children Exposed to Pesticides in Mexico" (Environmental Health Perspectives, Volume 106, Number 6, June 1998). Dr Cousens features this diagram of four drawings. There are two drawings by children who had minimal exposure to pesticides, and two who had a high exposure to them. The difference is astounding. The children share a genetic and cultural background, eat the same type of foods and drink the same water. Not only could the pesticide-free children draw better, they had better recall and dexterity.

Intensively farmed non-organic foods are often only fertilised with the three minerals necessary for quick harvests (nitrogen, phosphorus and potassium). Sometimes up to sixteen minerals are used but when you consider there are over 90 known minerals, you can see that this method of farming short-changes us. If you pick a wild edible plant (or well-loved organic one) you will find it bestowed with a multitude of trace minerals, and higher levels of vitamins and enzymes, all of which we need to thrive.

If eating a high-mineral diet really interests you, try growing your wheatgrass, peashoots, sprouts and vegetables in a dilute mixture of Ocean Grown. Ocean Grown is a concentrated solution of sea minerals and can be added to all growing plants. Sea water contains every mineral essential for life, and so we absorb more minerals from those foods when we eat them. It even makes the plants look and taste more vibrant. Ocean Grown says: "By restoring the full-spectrum of natural minerals, properly balanced, to the earth's soil, Ocean Grown will do its part in preserving the environment". If you can't find the Ocean Grown brand, then dilute your own sea water (one part sea water to ten parts water) and water your plants. You will even get more antioxidants in your food when you use sea water.

We always revert to raw foods

Our bodies are invigorated by and thrive on raw foods. Take away cultural programming and humans will normally only eat raw food. There are many stories of children who through highly unusual circumstances grew up away from "civilisation". Animals such as wolves have raised some of these children. Other children have fended for themselves, fully utilising their natural instincts to thrive in the wild.

These feral children nearly always ate exclusively raw food, and when discovered were often in peak physical health. A great example of this is Memmie LeBlanc, the Wild Girl of Songy. One evening in 1731 the villagers of Songy (in the Champagne region of France) were shocked when a girl around nineteen years old walked into the village. She was covered in rags and skins, wore a gourd leaf on her head and was armed with a short baton. It is thought that thirst drew her to the village after the region had suffered its worst drought in 50 years. She had survived for ten years in the forests.

According to Julia Douthwaite in *Rewriting The Savage*, Memmie could run with immense speed and her physical dexterity was highly advanced. She would amaze the villagers with her powers and could catch rabbits and hares at their request. She could swim like a duck and was extremely dexterous in diving for and catching fish, which she would bring ashore in her teeth to gut and eat immediately. She had survived almost exclusively on raw flesh, fish, roots, fruits, branches and leaves. "It was noticed that everything she ate, she ate raw". Although many tried, it was practically impossible to wean her onto any cooked food — she only ate raw and it seems her body knew what it needed.

There are other accounts of feral children with almost identical diets and traits and it proves almost always impossible or at least very difficult to get these children to eat a conventional western cooked diet. Indeed, according to Douthwaite, the attempts made to convert Memmie to a cooked diet very nearly cost her life.

Keep it in the family

Our culture has become dependent on fast, adulterated and processed foods. Preparing good, wholesome food is now alien to many parents and carers, and so subsequent generations remain disconnected from food preparation. In tribal communities around the world collecting foods and then preparing them takes centre stage. This process unites families and tribal units. Each generation is witness to the skills needed to eat naturally and healthily.

Even if good food is prepared in the home, there now seems to be less emphasis on sharing this exciting and valuable practice. Children benefit greatly when they're exposed to the magic of playing with ingredients, textures, flavours and smells. Given the chance, many children love to get involved. Evie does this all the time and I turn a blind eye to the mess, knowing that this is one of the most important lessons in her life. I'd love to see more kids in kitchens so they can in turn pass on the joys of real food to their offspring.

what is the raw food diet?

A raw food diet is the natural diet for all animals on this planet. 99.9 per cent of the world's population follow a raw food diet, which they've evolved to eat over millions of years. The other percentage, let's call them humans and their companion animals, eat cooked food. Cooked food is flawed in many ways. Consider the following:

Cooked food contains chemicals unknown to the human body, so the body pounces on them, creating an immune system response called leukocytosis. Multiply this by three meals a day, three snacks a day and countless drinks, and you will soon understand that your body is reacting as if it's in a perpetual state of attack. Over time this weakens the body and makes it sick. The sickness is an attempt at detox, which is often suppressed with drugs or more food. Over the years, a healthy baby develops disease after disease and as a teenager may develop acne, period pains, growing pains, bad breath and cellulite. The 99.9 per cent of the world's population who don't eat cooked food, let's call them wild animals and some primal societies, rarely get these symptoms. A typical UK teenager becomes an adult who eats lots of cooked foods and drinks lots of coffee and alcohol. He gets diabetes (about two million people have it in the UK), candida, arthritis, heart disease, obesity (60% chance) and cancer (about 35% chance). The 99.9 per cent of the world's population who eat raw food rarely get any of these diseases.

People on a raw food diet eat 100% raw, uncooked food. Many people find this a little difficult (often for social reasons) so they choose a 75-99 per cent raw food diet. Most raw foodists are vegetarian or vegan, but some eat raw fish and meat. I don't call myself a raw foodist any more: Evie and I are *ecstatic* foodists. We eat the way we do to feel as ecstatic as possible.

Raw foodism is the oldest diet in the world. For all species on the planet except humans and the animals they keep, it's the only diet available. It's the ultimate fast food diet — just pick and go!

The benefits of a high-raw or all-raw diet are clear:

- Increased energy
- Weight loss (or gain if you were too skinny)
- Diseases disappearing
- Happiness, and often ecstatic bliss

What you find on a raw foodist's dinner plate varies greatly. Aside from those who eat a balanced raw diet, there are natural hygienists, sproutarians, fruitarians, juicearians and living foodists. Most raw foodists eat a high proportion of organic or wild food in the belief that conventional food is more toxic and weaker.

Raw foods are cleansing, energy-giving, full of life and help people avoid disease associated with the Standard UK Diet (SUKD) and Standard American Diet (SAD). People who eat a high proportion of raw foods have a tell-tale glow that is the envy of all their friends. Raw foodists look to nature to get it right. And it's so simple.

Our meals are based on the following foods:

- Fruits, dried, fresh or frozen, especially wild
- Vegetables, dried or fresh, especially wild
- Seed sprouts (alfalfa, broccoli, radish, onion, sunflower, quinoa etc)

If you don't want to stop eating cooked foods, then make the decision to cut out microwaved foods and to have at least 51% raw food in each meal to stop yourself suffering from leukocytosis and a suppressed immune system.

- Micro greens (buckwheat, sunflower etc)
- Herbs and spices, fresh and dried, especially out of my garden
- Nuts and their butters (cashew, macadamia, pecan, hazel, walnut, brazil etc)
- Seeds and their butters (sunflower, sesame, hemp, flax, Salba etc)
- Ancient grains, soaked or ground (buckwheat, amaranth etc)
- Sea vegetables, often dried (Clearspring's Japanese sea vegetables is my favourite brand)
- Algaes, sometimes frozen, powdered or compressed into tablets (AFA algae, spirulina, chlorella etc)
- Ecstatic foods (cacao, maca, goji berries, Incan berries, wheatgrass, aloe vera, algae etc)

I sprinkle ecstatic foods onto all our meals, without fail. I usually have between one and three pints of green juice a day, though I don't kick myself if I don't make it for a few days. Evie has between half and one and a half pints of green juice a day, too. I know of no other way of getting enough essential minerals into a raw child to ensure correct growth. When pregnant or breastfeeding, one or two pints of green juice a day is wonderfully hydrating and nourishing. Cucumber juice is especially great for reducing water retention.

Special foods that we love

We should all reduce the environmental impact of our taste buds by eating locally sourced food where possible. Most of the foods Evie and I eat are locally grown, often wild, and in season. Having said that, we also love quite a few foods that aren't native to our country. Our diet includes some of the finest ecstatic foods on the planet. These are foods that have been revered by shamans, ancient peoples, modern locals and tourists alike. Daily, we add some or all of the following foods to our meals. This makes our diet infinitely interesting and nutritious. We love taking on the vibrational qualities of the foods and assimilating the ancient secrets contained within them.

Cacao

Since discovering raw chocolate in Maui in 2003, and co-writing *Naked Chocolate* with David Wolfe in 2005, I've been astonished at how quickly the raw food revolution has taken off. Cacao is the most nutrient-dense and antioxidant-rich food on the planet!

In *Naked Chocolate* we researched everything there is to know about raw cacao and created some great recipes. The introduction of the cacao bean created a bit of a stir in the raw world as well as the cooked world and it's changed the face of wholefood shops. The cacao I import comes from Peru. The farmers get a great price for supplying us with the best product. In fact, it's become so popular that the farmers have undertaken a big cacao tree planting project. Cacao trees really do save the world because they have to be grown in forest conditions, so the more cacao trees there are, the more forest there is. Cacao is truly a great ecstatic food, in a class of its own, and is the doorway to so many wonderlands. The cacao gods showed me that paradise is still here on earth, we just need to tap into it.

You can currently find raw cacao in a few guises, and all types go well with each other. There's the bean that you need to peel, which you can just pop into your mouth and enjoy (or drizzle a little raw agave nectar onto it first). There are the nibs, which are crushed and skinned beans. These are great for grinding up and adding to all kinds of sweet and savoury raw delights. There is cacao butter, a white block of pure raw healthy fat. This melts at mouth temperature so you can create real raw chocolates with it. And then there's raw chocolate powder — nibs slowly melted and ground at a temperature that doesn't cook the bean; when the fat and solids are separated, the solids are then ground into a fine powder. Apart from its culinary aspects this raw chocolate powder has an exceptionally high antioxidant content. In fact nothing else comes close with a massive 955 ORAC units per gram. Cooked chocolate powder only has 260 ORAC units per gram.

We know we need good fats in our diet, and they make up around 40% of a cacao bean, along with an abundance of sulphur and magnesium. We wrote about Chocolate Yoga in *Naked Chocolate* because cacao really does increase flexibility due to the magnesium and MAO inhibitors. Other chemicals help you become more powerful and allow you to practise for longer without tiring. We also discovered that researchers had found babies born to chocolate-eating mothers were happier. Small discoveries like this made us realise that chocolate is so utterly magical and we eat it with respect and love every day.

The raw power of cacao disappears in cooked chocolate and it becomes a drug. This is not good for children or adults. Though many may search for the natural high that is our birthright, they won't find it in cooked foods or drugs. This natural high is only available through the correct use of ecstatic foods such as chocolate, and other ecstatic activities such as yoga, breathing and loving. With these activities as your constant companions, you rediscover your natural higher state with no crash or comedown. Oh, to let the world know they can have their cake, eat it, lick the plate clean and go back for another slice!

The MAO inhibitors present in cacao also appear to diminish your appetite, so you really can lose weight on a diet of raw chocolate. Of course, in commercial chocolate, cooked fat and refined sugar doesn't help the waistline at all.

The best "science bit" part of cacao for me is the fact that it contains PEA (phenylethylamine). This is the chemical that we create and release when we are in love. It also helps to increase focus and alertness. I love making recipes with algae and cacao as they both contain PEA, and I can feel my mind sharpen immediately. It really helped me get my pre-Evie brain back (I thought getting my figure back was hard after having Evie, but it was nothing compared to wandering around for days not knowing what I was doing).

As well as making you feel like you're in love, cacao also blisses you out. The chemical responsible is called anandamide and is actually known as The Bliss Chemical. This neurotransmitter is present in cacao and is also produced naturally in the brain. Other elements of cacao slow the breakdown of anandamide, making you feel connected, chilled, blissful and happy for longer.

Goji berries

Little red jewels tasting a bit like cranberry and cherry, Evie delights in goji berries, dried or soaked in water for five minutes. I add them to many meals, including savoury ones. They're a super-nutritious ancient Chinese berry but they've been growing in UK hedgerows for centuries, known as The Duke Of Argyle's Tea Tree. Each plant yields around two kilos of fruit a year. Try growing some with your children in a pot or planted in your garden. They'll love picking and eating the fresh fruit.

Goji berries contain eighteen amino acids. They contain around 21 trace minerals, bursting with zinc, iron, copper, calcium, germanium, selenium and phosphorus. They have more beta carotene than carrots, and are the richest source of this vitamin A precursor. They also contain vitamins B1, B2, B6 and E.

Gojis are a real medicinal food and can help you with inflammation, immunity, strength, stamina (in all parts of your body) and hormone function. Just like cacao, they contain chemicals that aid rejuvenation. Gojis are known as a fountain of youth.

Maca

Maca (*Lepidium Peruvianum*) is a root vegetable indigenous to Peru, where it has been celebrated as a medicine and staple food for thousands of years. It is a cruciferous vegetable related to the carrot, radish and parsnip.

Maca contains surprisingly large amounts of vitamins, minerals and enzymes, and all eight essential amino acids. The amino acid content of this plant gives it an average protein content of around 14%. Maca has an impressive array of minerals, with notably high levels of bioavailable calcium. It also contains fair amounts of magnesium, silica and minerals.

The medicinal qualities of this plant are classified as being adaptogenic, meaning that it helps the body to deal with stress and bring bodily functions back to a normal state. For example, it will help raise thyroid function if it's too sluggish yet will subdue function if it's overactive. Adaptogens help to balance all bodily functions in a similar way.

In many traditional and conventional medical practices in Peru, Maca is used for male impotence, menopausal symptoms and general fatigue. This is due to its ability to normalise steroid hormones like testosterone, progesterone and oestrogen. Because of this it may also have the ability to slow the hormonal changes of ageing.

Hemp seeds

The hemp seed is one of the most nutritious substances in the world. Its complex array of nutrients is perfectly aligned for optimal human health. Its cultivation is good for the earth, as it helps to repair eroded and over-farmed land by binding the soil and fixing nitrogen. Mankind has eaten it for millennia. It's used to make clothes, rope, paper and fuel, and it is the number one component of many natural cosmetics.

There are three unique nutritional factors that make hemp one of my favourite ingredients. Firstly it contains about 35% fats, including omegas 3, 6 and 9. These essential fatty acids come in the ideal ratio for superior human health. Secondly it is loaded with trace minerals. Thirdly it contains the full array of essential amino acids and histidine, meaning it provides a complete protein for children and adults alike.

Hemp is available as whole seeds in their shells, shelled seeds, protein powder extract and oil. I find that one of the easiest ways of using hemp is in a smoothie, where I mix a handful of the shelled seeds with maca, chocolate, coconut water and fruit in the blender. I also make sprouted hemp mylk, which has to be one of the most nutritious ways to start the day.

Algae and seaweed

When life first formed here several billion years ago, our planet was a hostile and unforgiving place. Algae can take most of the credit for the turnaround. Plankton and single-celled organisms like algae literally ate their way through our ancient harsh environment and helped to convert it to the paradise in which we now live. These simple organisms formed the basis of life, and still ultimately support it.

Seaweed is becoming increasingly popular in our society. As so many minerals are now only abundant in the sea (due to intensive land farming methods), it makes sense to eat foods harvested from there. Choosing a diet rich in sea vegetables really boosts our intake of nutrients and trace elements, and even protects us from illness by helping us detoxify and heal.

Plankton make up, by biomass, perhaps the greater part of life on this earth, and contain minerals, proteins and other nutrients. Whales are able to consume 1,500,000 calories a day just by eating them along with some krill (which also feed entirely on plankton). Phytoplankton contains everything your body would need to regenerate neurochemicals and healthy new cells. This is a powerful food, which works with the body on a very deep level. We sprinkle marine phytoplankton onto our salads, and you can also add small amounts to water and sip it.

Algae are also guardians of the oceans, providing food for sea animals and humans. Rich in protein, there are several types of algae. All cyanobacteria (such as chlorella, spirulina and AFA) are now recognised to be of great importance to human health.

AFA (Aphanizomenon flos-aquae) means invisible, living, flower of water. It contains significant amounts of chlorophyll, vitamins, enzymes and minerals. This seems to be a brain food like no other, awakening our primordial past and helping us to embrace our ecstatic future. My favourite brands are Crystal Manna (flakes) and Blue Manna (high-PEA algae extract). E3Live is a freshly frozen liquid algae that children enjoy diluted in juice.

Chlorella, though sharing many of its cousins' attributes, has shown a tremendous ability to remove radiation from animals and to help humans detoxify dioxins. Chlorella contains genuine vitamin B12.

Spirulina is probably the most commonly known algae. It's a rich source of essential amino acids. Although few clinical trials have been conducted on humans it has been used on animals with some surprising results. Those with cancer, strokes, hayfever and brain deterioration have all benefited from spirulina. My one reservation with this food is that it contains vitamin B12 analogues. These are chemicals that look like B12 and fit into our B12 receptor sites, blocking real B12 from being absorbed. Because of this I recommend a few weeks off eating spirulina every now and then, whilst taking a high dose vitamin B12 supplement.

All seaweeds have been promoted for weight loss (by stimulating thyroid activity), boosting the immune system, decreasing blood sugar and cholesterol, increasing gastro-intestinal tract function, and for decreasing the symptoms of arthritic joint pains. My favourite seaweed by far is Clearspring's Japanese Sea Vegetable Salad, which is a mix of coloured seaweeds. Just soak it in water for ten minutes and it's ready to enjoy. I also love sea spaghetti, which comes as long strands of tagliatelle-style seaweed. After soaking in water for an hour, it makes the base of one of the most satiating raw meals on the planet.

Look out for kelp, dulse and laver, our native edible seaweeds. I use kelp powder every week in one of Evie's meals. It provides iodine and many other minerals. It has a dense flavour, and a quarter of a teaspoon will enhance any savoury dish.

In health food shops you may find arame, a kind of kelp. This is the mildest tasting of all sea vegetables and it's rich in fibre and low in carbohydrates and sodium. It's precooked, so don't use it if you want to be 100% raw.

Wakame, another kind of kelp, is widely used in making soup and can be soaked and eaten raw. Try it with a vinegary marinade or pine nut sauce. I really like this one. I used to chew this up for Evie and spit it into her mouth when she was about eighteen months old.

Seagreens is a proprietary brand of powdered seaweed, containing Arctic wild wrack seaweeds (Pelvetia, Fucus and Ascophyllum). It comes as a granular powder or in capsules. I add a capsule to all of Evie's salads and dressings, and I also put the granules in breads and crackers. It boosts the nutritional content of all her meals. The iodine content is low in Seagreens, so you can use it every day, unlike kelp.

Nori is the universal name for various species of red algae, and normally comes in sheets ready to be filled. It's one of the most common "sandwich breads" in our house (others being lettuce, hollowed out cucumbers and cabbage). If you haven't sampled the delights of nori rolls filled with salads, hummous, tahini, sprouted seeds and avocado, with a side dish of tahini and shaved ginger, then you're missing out. Very often Evie has a nori roll for breakfast. As she gets older she likes to fill it herself. I only intervened once as she piled it high with raspberries, Engevita and tamari.

Green nori is toasted. Black nori is either raw or very briefly roasted, but you wouldn't know the difference by looking at the packaging.

You may wonder about sea pollution and sea foods. All the companies that retail through health food stores seem to have an excellent track record for harvesting foods only from pristine areas. The UK law on organic certification doesn't allow for some of these sea and lake products to be certified as they are not cultivated. You may see the same products in the USA with organic certification because their laws are different. Always research your sea foods carefully and go for the best you can get.

Wild foods

How many times do we go to the stupormarket to fill our cupboards with groceries that have been picked weeks earlier, shipped half way around the world, irradiated, over-packaged and over-priced? Imagine a world where the freshest, most nutritious foods grew at our feet. These foods were free for the taking whenever we wanted them. The variety and flavours changed through the year. They gave us the nutrients we needed. No matter how much we ate, more seemed to grow in its place... You don't need to imagine, you are living in paradise.

Throughout the year it is possible to go foraging for a gourmet's hamper of delights. From the first shoots of nettle (which don't sting if juiced or rolled) and dandelion in spring, through to the heavier denser greens later in the year such as wild garlic and mallow, to linden leaves and borage in the early summer. Herbs, elderflowers and comfrey will follow. Some mushrooms will start coming out as soon as June, but do your research carefully: although most are harmless, one or two are deadly and you don't have nine lives.

Later in the year things get sweet and sticky with an abundance of berries. Raspberries, blackberries, strawberries, logan berries, blueberries, wild cherries and dewberries. Then come the apples and pears. In this country we are blessed with so many varieties of the most delicious apples you could imagine. Come November it's time to squirrel away bucket loads of nuts to see you through the cold spell. Beech nuts, sweet chestnut, hazelnuts and walnuts are great for eating and even the humble acorn can be used to make drinks with. Bright red yew berries decorate the frosty winter landscape, and they are delicious and nutritious once you remove the highly poisonous pip. If you're not in the UK you'll have different choices, yet nature will still bestow abundance all around you.

These days it's unlikely that you'll be able to live 100% from nature but the more you can do it the better. Don't collect anything too close to roads because of pollution. Remember not to take everything, either, otherwise there may be nothing to collect the following year. Nutritionally and taste-wise nothing comes close to eating wild food.

Is the raw food lifestyle expensive?

Your health doesn't have a price. Eating raw can be expensive, but if you're resourceful it doesn't have to be. I know people from all walks of life who make raw living seem easy simply because they love the benefits it brings. I also know people who use every excuse under the sun to *not* eat raw foods, even though they say they want to. Money is just one of those excuses; if you want to eat raw, you will. Here are some tips for eating raw food on a budget:

- Grow a huge variety of sprouts on your windowsill
- Plant some fruit trees
- Grow greens in your garden or in tubs
- Forage
- Garden share: find like-minded friends, pool your resources and pool your harvest
- Visit the market at the end of the day when fresh food is often reduced in price
- Set up an organic distribution service for yourself and likeminded friends, then buy at wholesale prices
- Work in exchange for food

In UK households around a third of all purchased food is thrown away. Evie and I rarely throw food away. Here's how we save and recycle it:

- Make pancakes out of leftover smoothies in the dehydrator
- Make fruit leathers and dried fruit pieces in the dehydrator to store our harvests for future months
- Dehydrate spring leaves and make green superfood powders for future months
- Make soups out of leftover salads and vegetable meals

Any wasted food gets composted, and then recycled back into our garden.

Do you need special equipment?

You don't need special equipment but many people find the following especially helpful. Dehydrators, high-speed blenders (I favour the Vita-Prep 3), juicers (I love my Green Power Kempo) and several other gadgets are often found in the raw foodist's kitchen. Find more information about the gadgets I use every day in the *Alchemical tools* section just before the recipes.

Take your time with buying stuff, and remember that you can get by with just your hands!

Will I become deficient in anything if I eat just raw food?

You can be deficient in nutrients on any diet. The SUKD (Standard UK Diet) is low in phyto-nutrients, B12, EFAs, vitamins, minerals, antioxidants and water.

The nutrients to watch out for on a raw vegan diet include vitamins B12, D and K2, choline, iron, calcium and essential fatty acids. It's particularly important to consciously add these to a pregnant mother's and growing child's diets. I address all these issues in detail in the *Nutrition and your child's future* section of this book.

Ecstatic foods, hemp protein powder and juiced or blended greens will cover your child's protein needs when eaten regularly and sufficiently. There is no need to eat animals to get enough protein. I've been a vegan for about 21 years and only ever suspected a protein deficiency when I was eating a high-fruit diet (something I don't recommend!) There are also lifelong vegans and raw vegans who are in tip-top health, but you need to take supplementation seriously as it's not natural for us to be 100% vegan.

Can children eat nothing but raw food?

Humans have been habitually cooking their food for just a few thousand years. All animals except humans (and their companion animals) eat 100% raw food, and they've done so since time began. The young of all wild animals gestate as raw and grow up raw, with no exceptions. And most of them grow up as nature intended — fit, strong, and able to do what they need to flourish.

Humans, as they process and manipulate their food more and more every year, by comparison, are no longer thriving. Increasingly more are ill, violent, depressed, malformed and infertile.

As raw food is natural, and as all other animals thrive on raw food, then yes, human children can also thrive on raw food. Many children have been and are being raised successfully on a raw food diet — Evie is one of them.

In fact, considering the toxicity levels of our planet now, if children don't eat a diet high in nutrient dense raw foods, then their chances of a healthy future are limited. Raw foodism isn't just a pie-in-the sky celebrity lifestyle fad, it's the diet we evolved to eat and the only diet that will stop us sinking into an oblivious pit of viruses, bacteria, fungus, mould and toxicity.

Just remember that children have some different nutritional needs to adults, so your raw food diet will have to be modified for them, just as a cooked food diet would be. As with all diets, proceed with knowledge and care.

What about supplements?

Bringing up a raw vegan child requires dedication and a good understanding of nutrition. Children should never be our experiments, regardless of how well-intentioned our actions are. They need a diet high in essential fatty acids, vitamins, minerals and protein found in non-sweet or semi-sweet fruits, vegetables, nuts, ecstatic foods, seeds, sea vegetables, sprouts, herbs and juices. They need breastfeeding for as long as possible. Most importantly for excellent health, raw vegan children need supplements for the few, but essential, elements that are missing or low in a vegan diet. I outline these in the *Nutrition and your child's future* section.

I feel that the raw food diet is the perfect diet; it's certainly the original diet. However, being vegan means you need to accept a little help, otherwise your family will not remain in optimal condition. Your child could suffer for life as a consequence, so please supplement your child if you're raising her vegan, raw or not. There is a chance, even with supplementation, that your raw vegan child will not flourish. If you see any signs of this, please refer to a nutritionist or dietician immediately. In the UK, GPs and dieticians will work with you to support your lifestyle choice. Your solutions may differ, but if you get good results, they won't harass you.

The healthiest children I've seen are raw vegetarian, eating some eggs and milk products. Please be open to the possibility of feeding your child these products to keep her fully healthy and happy if supplementation doesn't have great results for your child.

How do I start eating raw food?

There are some great raw recipe books, and all of the meals in this book are perfect for adults too. I've published over 500 raw vegan recipes, so you never need to have the same raw meal twice.

I've coached many people with raw food, and the most successful method has been this: change one meal at a time. Become comfortable with that meal, and then change the next one.

For example, you could first alter your breakfast. Make smoothies, eat fruit, make juices, have raw muesli with nut mylk etc.

Then when you're happy with that, alter your lunch. Make cabbage burritos, lettuce or nori wraps, salads, dehydrated goodies such as burgers or crackers with hummous and guacamole. Top it all with a mix of ecstatic foods such as purple corn extract, Seagreens, Crystal Manna, pink salt, digestive enzymes and spirulina.

Then alter your evening meal, dipping into raw recipe books when you have time. Our favourite evening meal is *Stir crazy* (and its many variants), which we make earlier in the day and dehydrate until tea time. This gives us a warm and comforting evening meal, which we serve with dehydrated bread, salad or nori.

Making your snacks raw could mean eating fresh or dried fruits, nuts or seeds, or raw chocolate, or enjoying vegetable sticks with dips. *Seaseeds* is our favourite nibbly snack.

Finally, including ecstatic foods every day will ensure you get more minerals and other nutrients that may be missing from a normal raw and cooked diet. Incan berries contain vitamin B12. Goji berries have over 10 per cent protein. Maca has over 10% calcium. These foods are exceptional in their nutritional make-up and we should take advantage of them at every opportunity.

If you're still questioning raw foods, consider the following:

- If you can't eat food raw and unprocessed (like kidney beans and potatoes), ask yourself "Is this food designed for humans?"
- Watch food as it's cooking. See the water disappear, the colours fade and the textures change.
- Compare how your body feels when you eat raw food compared to when you eat cooked food. Which meal makes you more energetic, more alert, happier? Which food sedates you and makes you tired?
- Ask yourself if you're as healthy and happy as you could be. If the answer's no, then add ecstatic foods into every meal.

Do I have to go all-raw, and all-Vegan?

Most people who get into raw food don't eat a 100% raw diet for various reasons. The great news is that you can receive many of the benefits of raw foodism without the dedication that's required to be entirely raw: just eat at least 51% in weight of raw food at every meal. Why does this work? Because that magic number allows your body to recognise enough of the food to digest it, rather than attack it.

When you eat cooked food, your body doesn't recognise it: it causes leukocytosis. This is where white blood cells are released into the stomach to deal with the "invader". Your body doesn't know the difference between cooked food and a virus. Having leukocytosis many times a day is the reason why our bodies can end up in a terrible auto-immune self-attacking state. Imagine the lift from your body's load if half of your food was raw and you didn't suffer from leukocytosis. Knowing this, we can now easily choose to create better health for our whole family.

Organic or wild is better than non-organic. Home-grown is better than stupormarket bought food. Find foods grown with love, because that's the frequency you want your child to eat. A meal cooked with love is better than a raw lettuce grown with resentment in a polytunnel.

Just remember the magic number: 51% in weight of raw food at each meal. Easy. Easy. Easy.

If you feed your child cooked food, it shouldn't be calorie-laden and nutrient-deficient. Choose whole foods that are lightly cooked, minimally processed and mixed in with lots of raw foods.

Sweet potatoes, buckwheat pasta, steamed vegetables, hummous, wild rice and sprouted breads are all great choices for the child who eats some cooked food.

There are raw foodists who eat insects, meat, fish, dairy, eggs, honey, and other animal products. Raw doesn't mean vegan or vegetarian. If you aren't vegan or vegetarian, then eggs are better than animal milk, fish is often better than land meat and bee pollen and honey are good nutritional choices. Take care feeding raw animal products to your child as they are loaded with pathogens. You could use a Zappicator on any raw animal food before you eat it.

Raw mother and visionary Tish Clifford has researched vegan versus non-vegan diets. She says: "If there are problems with digestion then I would suggest that is because they are vegan. Vegans can find it hard to digest the quantities needed to maintain great teeth and good dense growth". Chewing your child's food and fermenting food will greatly assist in your child's digestive process.

How to start a child on raw food

Maximising your child's instinct

Do you remember when you were little and you'd do anything to avoid eating boiled cabbage and sprouts? Often, young children won't eat their vegetables because they've been overcooked and they taste and smell sulphurous. Children act instinctively and can easily decide if something's going to be good for them. Evie has always enjoyed green juice. In the beginning I'd involve her in the juicing process and she'd get a sweet treat if she drank all her juice. After a short while she'd ask for the juice and then drink mine too. It wasn't long before I had to start making extra. I figured that if she ate nothing else "good" all day, she was getting a huge amount of greens in the most easy-to-assimilate form.

Which came first, the chickweed or the cress?

If you want to start your children on green juice, mix a small amount of it into some juice that they already drink. If they love apple juice, try making apple and celery or apple and cucumber first. Slowly and

gradually increase the greens to include kale, parsley, coriander, greens from your garden, rocket, watercress and spinach. Soon your children will get a taste for it as it's so nutritious. If your children are hooked on sweet-tasting food then it will take longer for them to enjoy green juices. Persevere and you will reap your reward: vibrant children with the best taste in food on the planet.

Another way to add juice to your child's drink is to make a strong green juice, pour it into ice cube trays and freeze it. Pop one cube into any drink before serving and she can have fun watching the green iceberg crashing around the cup as she drinks.

Children need to connect to the earth and see where their food comes from. Wander around your garden with them or go to the woods. Take a wild food book and a bag. See if you can fill your bag with edible plants. Eat the leaves and fruits there and then. Make a salad, pie, smoothie or juice when you get back to your kitchen. These free activities help you spend essential time with your children, while they eat and learn the art of self-sufficiency. Perfect!

In the autumn I take Evie down the lane by my house. We pick brambles (blackberries) off the bushes and eat them. Evie comes home purple-faced and ecstatic from her wild food walk, and my kitchen remains clean!

One of the most rewarding pastimes you can have with your child is to grow food with her. If you don't have a garden you can grow cress, sprouts and herbs inside. If you do have a garden, or even a patio, you can grow countless varieties of edible plants. Once you get over-excited about growing foods you can get an allotment, share space with neighbours, grow community food gardens or just keep foraging in the woods. Consider planting fruit trees wherever you go, too. Children love revisiting them as they grow up and become abundant with fruit.

Getting a child excited about raw food

So you're into raw food and you've read all the benefits, but what happens if your child isn't in such a hurry to give up his pasta and tomato sauce? I have three nephews and each one has gone though a (lengthy) stage of calling me weird. They've also gone through stages of letting me feed them the food I eat. My eldest nephew loves avocados, thanks to my dad. My youngest loves raw chocolate. The middle one, well, he still calls me weird. However, when I looked after him for a fortnight at the age of fourteen I did get him eating a few raw vegetables before he had his beans on toast. All older children will eat some raw food if you explain the benefits clearly.

Making food appealing is easier than you may think; yet the starting point will be different for each child. Some children are fussy eaters; some are hearty eaters. Here are some tried and tested pointers for small children:

- **Silly plates**: This involves doing anything surreal with food. Children love the unexpected. Put food on dolly's plates, or use oversized and mismatching cutlery. Try feeding dolly first. Feed your belly button. Let your child feed you. Reverse roles, act like your child and call your child Mummy.
- **Fishing**: When Evie was small we put goji berries, raisins and other dried foods in the bath. Evie fished them out, and then ate them.
- **Where food comes from**: Get your child involved with gardening, wild fruit hunting, eating edible flowers, growing pots of sprouts, and making animal sprouts (use tights to make a face and grow sprouts inside. The sprouts will come out like hair all over the "animal").
- **Hide and seek**: I hide little food parcels around the house or garden for Evie to seek out.
- **Blankie picnics**: When it's cold outside, we lay down a blanket or tablecloth and have a picnic inside with party cups and plates. We get dressed up and eat to party music in the presence of many dollies.
- **Eating in the car**: It's funny how children will eat in a car when they refuse to eat at home. Take advantage of it by preparing pots of cut up vegetables for all your car journeys.
- **Eating around the stupormarket**: That stupormarket trolley came in so handy when I couldn't get Evie to sit still and eat. Avocados, bananas, punnets of berries and even cucumbers got demolished before we'd arrive at the checkout. I kept the labels to scan, though!
- **Making food together**: This is a really important practice. When Evie was really little I'd put the juicer and cutting board on the floor. She'd eat as I made the food. She still does it now, sitting on the worktop. Make dough from ground flax and water and get them to shape it. Dehydrate it to make nibbly biscuits.
- **Funny faces**: We use sprouts for hair, a tomato for the nose, red pepper for the lips and olives on cucumber rounds for the eyes. Suddenly, a drab salad snack is appealing and fun.

Starting a baby on raw foods

If your baby isn't yet eating solids, then it's even easier for you to introduce raw foods when weaning time comes. If she's never eaten cooked foods, she won't miss them. However, if you eat cooked foods don't expect your child not to notice. It'll be in your breastmilk, on your breath and on your clothes. Practise what you preach.

What are the first foods?

Evie's first food was organic papaya with breastmilk. Making the new food recognisable by adding a familiar flavour works well during all transitional stages. Sitting your child on your knee facing you makes the situation feel like a breastfeeding session, so she'll feel more comfortable, confident and at ease.

"I sometimes chew lettuce or spinach for her and then feed it to her. I know that is something I can only share with you and my husband. Everyone else out there would think I was insane and filthy."
— A Mummy, by email.

Give the food on a spoon if you need to, but it's best scooped up on a clean finger, so you know it's the right temperature and you still get that intimate connection with your baby.

Some of Evie's other first foods were: bananas (go steady as they're constipating in large amounts and can cause extreme pain for your baby), avocados, mangoes, wheatgrass juice, spirulina and raw carob powder, all mixed up in varying combinations. There are many other soft fruits that are good blended, such as berries, durian, young coconut meat and its water, peaches, plums and so on.

8-12 months

To the above foods you could add two or three teaspoons of sprouted puréed quinoa, a quarter of a teaspoon of maca, a teaspoon of mesquite powder, half a teaspoon of algae, a pinch of marine phytoplankton or a quarter of a teaspoon of hemp protein powder. Go steady: these foods are powerful and young children are still getting most of what they need from breastmilk at this age.

Look at the Recipes section for more ideas about what to first feed your baby.

I frequently pre-chewed Evie's food when she was smaller. It's a natural practice that reduces the possibility of choking. It also helps children digest the food, as your enzymes start the digestion process for them.

Evie had all of the foods I mention above from seven months (along with breastmilk) up to about thirteen months. At that point she became one of those...

Toddlers!

Toddlers spend masses of energy and lose their baby fat as they climb, jump, roll, run, play and generally flail and flap.

Because of the increase in movement they need to start eating more nutrient-dense foods along with the familiar nutrient-rich breastmilk.

As a 16-month-old toddler Evie loved chunks of avocado, cucumber, dehydrated nut and sea vegetable burgers, mangoes, bananas, nuts (she would overeat on these, so I had to limit them), apples, carrots, broccoli, cauliflower, dehydrated cookies, nut mylks with ecstatic foods added, various green superfoods, durian, green vegetable juices, tomatoes, sea vegetables, various raw food bars, and lots more. I also made her light raw chocolates and other raw chocolate delights, which she adored in very small amounts.

As you can see, even at such a young age Evie ate a wide variety of foods. Her two main superfood mixes contained over 60 ingredients, and all the food I gave her was organic wherever possible. We ate wild food when out walking, and it was easy making a small packed lunch for when Evie was looking after some other adult.

A typical day for Evie's food at 21 months

- Breastmilk throughout the night.
- ½ cup of cashew nuts and water on waking (she often made me chew them for her and spit them into her mouth).
- Water.
- 1 small cup of freshly squeezed orange juice.
- A couple of veggie chips.
- Water.
- Breastmilk.
- ½ cup of soaked/sprouted buckwheat.
- Breastmilk.
- 1 banana.
- Breastmilk.

- ½ avocado with ½ cup of mixed sprouts rolled in ½ a nori sheet, topped with about ½ a teaspoon of Crystal Manna.
- Water.
- 2 cups of raspberries.
- Breastmilk.
- ½ avocado with ½ cup of mixed sprouts rolled in ½ a nori sheet, topped with about ½ a teaspoon of Crystal Manna (again).
- Water.
- 5 walnuts.
- Water.
- 1 choccie brownie.
- Bed, with breastmilk throughout the night.

Beyond toddlerhood

Omitting "empty" foods such as pasta and potatoes gives us the opportunity to get more of the good stuff in. It's essential that your child enjoys good quality fat and protein-rich foods. The consumption of soaked (preferably fermented) nuts and seeds needs to be high and continuous.

The big differences

What do you tell the 'authorities'?

Not too long ago parents used to fear admitting to the authorities that they were bringing their children up as vegetarian or vegan. However, because the vegetarian and vegan charities have worked so hard at successfully getting those diets understood and approved of, health visitors are much more understanding.

Raw food nutrition is still a mystery to health authorities. This may mean that you face an inquisition from your health visitor. My only advice is to supplement your child in the way I've outlined in this book, and to offer a broad array of foods. Ensuring your child has all his nutritional needs fulfilled will make it unlikely that you come under scrutiny.

Please note that my information isn't 100% prescriptive, it's experiential. As with any food lifestyle, please proceed with care, monitor the changes, and consult your healthcare practitioner if your child shows signs of deficiency.

What about parties and other sociable times?

Picnics and packed lunches

When Evie was about fourteen months old she started to attend a local, farm-based nursery for two afternoons a week. The nursery staff did everything they could to help Evie settle in and be accepted amongst her peers, despite her different lifestyle. I was happy to see her mixing with other children and forming relationships with them. Adult company all the time wasn't right for her. This seemed like a good solution. All the children ate "healthy" meals provided by the nursery. The snacks were fruit and then they had a cooked meal in the afternoon. Evie felt half-normal at snack time, sharing fruit with other children. Then the rest of the time, she had her packed lunch.

Her packed lunches were varied and they took me ten minutes to make. There was a "no nut" policy at the nursery, which made it harder as I couldn't pack pre-made burgers and the like. I always put in more than she needed (that's what mums do), and I often used the leftovers in our evening meal. Evie eats much more fruit than I do, and I feel that's natural for children.

Her typical packed lunch was:

- 2 bananas.
- 1 bag of goji berries mixed with hemp seeds, pumpkin seeds and sunflower seeds.
- 1 little box of raisins (not coated in oil).
- 1 tub of mixed salad (usually something like broccoli, celery, avocado, cucumber with a dressing of miso, Blue Manna, hemp seed butter and Seagreens).
- 1 carton of coconut water.
- 1 tub of crudités, such as carrots, peppers and courgettes.
- 1 chunk of raw white chocolate.

I offered her this amount and variety each day so she could feel more comfortable at nursery, choosing what she wanted rather than eating what was served. Even at this age children really know what they need and we should respect rather than suppress their instincts.

When we go to other people's houses we often take a packed lunch. I make this as simple as possible but I always take more than we need so other people can try our food.

Here's an example of a picnic that we'd take with us:

- 1 tub of guacamole, made with avocado, Blue Manna, hemp seeds, tomatoes and coriander.
- 1 tub of crudités such as cucumber, carrot, courgette and peppers.
- 1 tub of olives.
- 1 tub of raw chocolates.
- 1 tub of flax crackers.
- Fruit such as bananas, berries, oranges and apples.
- Drinks.

We never eat as well when we're away as we do at home, but the food is always healthy and tasty and it meets our needs at the time.

Missing out and little compromises

As your child gets older she'll want to know why she can't eat the same food as others around her. Tell her the truth, without being judgemental about the choices of others. I say to Evie that cooked food makes people poorly, unhappy and overweight. I tell her it ruins

your brain. I say that a tiny bit here and there is OK, but it's not OK to eat it all the time. As I believe in the power of positive affirmations, I also tell her that our food makes us strong, wild, free, clever and happy.

I'm convinced Evie doesn't miss out when surrounded by children eating different things. When she was younger, if someone gave her something she'd come up to me and say "Mummy, am I allowed this?" When she was three, she'd say to people "I'm not allowed that." Often she'd call it duck food and confuse everyone. She knows she eats differently. We were putting some stickers on some paper once and there was a sweetie sticker. "I don't like sweets" she said, pulling a face. She's never eaten them.

When Evie was just over three years old, she helped my dad make pasta and tomato sauce. She really wanted to try it so I gave her a small bowl of it. She loved it. Then she fell asleep. A couple of hours later she woke up, screaming with earache and crying. She didn't sleep for the rest of the evening. It was a lesson for both of us.

When Evie turned three I allowed her occasional tofu and soya milk. When she turned four, I made some other changes to her diet, which you can read in the *All about Evie* section. She doesn't need this cooked food but she likes the change, and it's convenient for other people when they're looking after her. I can feed Evie filling and nutritious food, but her dad and other relatives struggle with raw food eating. If Evie eats cooked food then I make sure she keeps it light. The pasta experience goes to show that not all cooked food is equal, and white wheat pasta must be amongst the worst of all because there's no nutrition in it and it's very gluey in the body.

Evie's Christmases

Evie has had four Christmases at the time of writing. She was just under five months old when she experienced her first, and was still fully breastfed. Of course, she woke up the minute I put my food on the table. I breastfed her as I was eating my Christmas dinner, so she got to experience it that way.

I've never been able to be around turkey on Christmas Day. I don't understand how the celebration of someone we call our saviour is masked by the total gluttony and carnage that a UK Christmas has become. For this reason I never share Christmas dinner with traditional people. I can handle people eating meat at other times, but not at Christmas as it pains me so much.

Evie's second Christmas was spent in our new house. She fell asleep just before dinner was served, so we said shush to the crackers as we pulled them so as not to wake her.

I'd made Evie lots of Christmas food such as little raw cookies. Over the previous two weeks she'd enjoyed all these along with her favourites such as clementines (suck juice, spit pulp, repeat), avocado with Crystal Manna blue-green algae, tomato and banana. Actually she ate lots more than that and I marvelled at the variety that she got through.

Evie's third Christmas was very exciting. I made my first raw gourmet Christmas meal, having previously only had fruits such as durian or special salads. We enjoyed goji and chestnut sauce, pecan nut loaf, cauliflower cheeze, wilted cabbage and parsley, "fried" mushrooms and mushroom gravy. Evie actually ate a fair amount of it, but I was more surprised to see her daddy tucking in. After all, it wasn't Stagg Chili. I made a lovely pudding of leftover chocolate cake, agave nectar, goji berries, coconut flakes and real gold flakes. It looked beautiful but we were far too full to eat it. I enjoyed it later in the evening when Evie was busy playing with her cousins.

Evie's fourth Christmas was almost too exciting for her. She was nearly three and a half and blossoming into a personality-overloaded young lady. Our dinner was a raw creamed wild mushroom tart, gravy and Christmas vegetables. Evie didn't eat much of it, yet Matt and I loved it. At this time Evie would only eat something if she knew exactly what it was, which occasionally drove me bonkers. So we packed up our leftovers and went to my parents' for Christmas evening. Later on Evie ate simply, yet abundantly, and I enjoyed the rest of the pie.

Evie's birthdays

Evie's first birthday party combined her naming ceremony and our house-warming party. Annette was living with us and working for me at the time. She created a raw birthday cake and several cooked and raw vegan dishes. Evie was too young to be curious about food, so I was happy with that. We had relatives from Hull staying, and many people who normally ate the SUKD, so the hot vegan chilli that my mum brought was OK for them and cheaper for us. We enjoyed many dips, salads, and raw sweeties.

Evie's second birthday was an all-raw chocolate tea party. As Evie was more into food I decided that her birthday spread should be all-raw. I made a chocolate and maca ice-cream, raw bite-sized chocolates, a chocolate and blueberry cheesecake which looked like a clear midnight sky, and other chocolatey foods. We served homemade lemonade made with fizzy water, Brazilian ginseng and agave nectar. Evie loved digging in, as did all the guests. I made sure she had lots of greens after the party. I didn't indulge in party bags or other gifts for the children guests; I'm not one for tradition and people know that, so they don't expect anything normal from me. I don't think gimmicky land-fill toys deserve a place in the birthday party of a mini-eco-warrioress.

For her third birthday the best gift was the hot August sunshine after a miserable July. Her second best gift was a goji plant. We had another all-raw spread with a wonderful Quantum Cake courtesy of Raw Living. At this point I'd realised that I didn't have to do everything and could stretch to buying a cake for my daughter's birthday! Evie had fun all day and still talks about it now.

Evie's fourth birthday saw sunshine and friends appear in our garden with perfect timing. She chose some disco music and enjoyed showing off her toys to her three little friends. I made a cake laced with ecstatic foods, and everyone adored it. We had half cooked, half raw food on the table, all vegan. It was much easier to prepare this kind of food. Evie had a little duck food, and all the normals were satiated.

Further information

Baby Greens — Michaela Lynn. This is a great experiential book with simple recipes and fun things to do.

Rainbow Green Live Food Cuisine — Dr Gabriel Cousens. This book is Gabriel's best work in my opinion. It is an up-to-date bible on raw food. The recipes are stunning, and those suitable for children are highlighted.

Food for Free — Richard Mabey. This is the UK's most popular wild food book. Pictures and descriptions allow you to accurately identify many wild foods. Richard also gives suggestions on preparing and eating the food.

Sea Energy Agriculture — Dr Maynard Murray. Maynard was a pioneer way before his time. This book was lost for decades before being revived. His work revolves around using diluted sea water in plants to create mineral rich harvests.

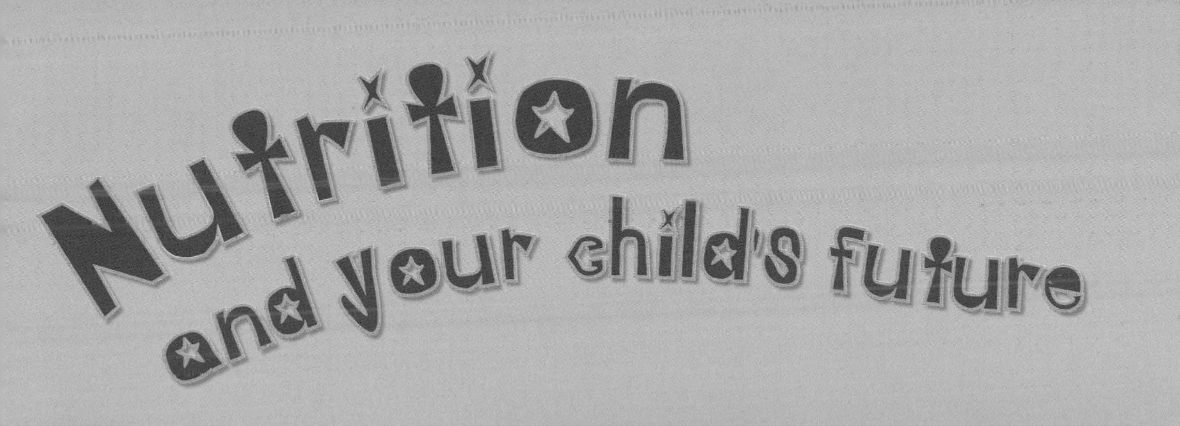
Nutrition
and your child's future

The one truth is that you are what you eat. Let your child be wild, strong, free and full of life force. That's much better, I'm sure you'll agree, than letting him be a couch potato.

The differences between an adult's raw diet and a child's raw diet aren't great, but they are important. Children grow at a rapid rate whereas adults just need to renew and repair. A typical western cooked diet quickly goes wrong when people eat food relieved of most of its nutrients. I call people who eat like this "overweight starving people", and they can be easily identified as the ones staring in the fridge for something more to eat despite having just polished off two rounds of pasta. Because our bodies need an abundance of nutrients, and because most western food is now nutrient-deficient, people unconsciously overeat in a vain attempt to find nutrients. This is why obesity is now so common. Scientists and those making trillions of pounds out of the phenomenon of our fat society will tell you a million different stories — all the while selling you their ideas, books, pills and potions.

A raw food diet, with care taken over some nutrients, allows a child to flourish in unique and special ways. The lack of trans-fats and the abundance of ecstatic fatty acids helps the brain reach its full potential. The lack of cooked cow milk and wheat allows the body to remain mucous-free. The lack of potatoes and pasta ensures that the child doesn't put on artificial weight, disguising the beginnings of an overweight starving person.

Basic nutritional requirements

The major requirements for toddlers from one year of age to three:

Nutrient	Amount	Symptoms of too little	Symptoms of too much *
Calories	about 1300	Loss of body fat, loss of muscle tissue	Infant obesity
Protein	16g	Weight loss, fatigue, high heart rate	Excess urea, back pain, kidney damage
Vitamin A	400mcg	Immune, skin, hair and eye problems	Liver damage
Vitamin C	40 mg	Weakness, swollen gums, nosebleeds, scurvy	Impossible — vitamin C is water soluble
Vitamin B1 (Thiamin)	0.7 mg	Beriberi, appetite loss, muscle pains	Difficulty breathing, anaphylactic shock
Vitamin B2 (Riboflavin)	0.8 mg	Cracked lips, sore mouth, anaemia	Impossible — vitamin B2 is water soluble
Vitamin B3 (Niacin)	9 mg	Weakness, lack of appetite, digestive problems	Flushing, tingling skin, diabetes symptoms
Vitamin B6	1.0 mg	Fatigue, anaemia, seizures	Nerve damage to arms and legs
Vitamin B12	0.5 mcg	Anaemia, palpitations, weak fast pulse, jaundice, vertical ridges in nails, speech delay	Impossible — vitamin B12 is water soluble
Vitamin D	1000 IU	Muscles pains/weakness, bow legs, seizures, cavities, bone deformities	Stomach cramps, vomiting, organ damage (rare)
Vitamin E	10mcg	Nerve damage (rare)	Fatigue, nausea, headache, weakness
Vitamin K2	55mcg	Stunted growth, facial deformities, cavities, heart problems, easy bruising	None known
Calcium	800mg	Malabsorption, tingling in extremities	Diarrhoea, dark stools
Iron	10 mg	Skeletal problems, anaemia, breathlessness, feeling cold, dizziness, low IQ	Dehydration, dark/bloody stools
DHA	300mg	Depression, flaking nails, low IQ, brain and heart dysfunction, arthritis, maybe Alzheimer's, ADHD, some cancers.	None recorded, but seek GPs advice if diabetic or with heart disease.

* Unless large quantities of supplements are taken it is usually highly unlikely to overdose on these vitamins.

Here is an at-a-glance table of where to find the above nutrients:

Nutrient	Sources
Calories	Everything apart from celery and water
Protein	Legumes, grains, nuts, seeds (especially hemp)
Vitamin A	Red, orange or yellow vegetables, leafy green vegetables
Vitamin C	Fresh fruit, salad, vegetables, all green leafy vegetables
Vitamin B1 (Thiamin)	Yeast, wholemeal products, rice, peanuts
Vitamin B2 (Riboflavin)	Green leafy vegetables
Vitamin B3 (Niacin)	Nuts, yeast extract
Vitamin B6	Bananas, beans, wholegrains
Vitamin B12	Seaweed, algae, miso, maca — but only in small amounts, supplements
Vitamin D	Sunlight, nettles, supplements
Vitamin E	Wheatgerm oil, almonds, sunflower seeds, sunflower oil, avocado
Vitamin K2	Milk, eggs, butter, natto, supplements
Calcium	Broccoli, dark leafy vegetables
Iron	Pumpkin seeds, sesame seeds, quinoa, pine nuts

Two amino acids are essential to children only: arginine (which is found in chocolate, buckwheat and wheatgerm amongst other foods) and histidine (found in rice, wheat and rye and others). Goji berries contain both amino acids.

Why supplement?

I feel the same as most people regarding supplements: I'd much rather get all my nutrients from food. However, food doesn't have the same nutrients as in days gone by. This is why I concentrate Evie's food by juicing, and it's one reason why I supplement her. Due to the vast array of nutrients in greens, if you eat enough of them, you get enough of most nutrients. Please do all you can to get green juices into your child at an early age.

Although most vegans accept that vitamin B12 is an issue for everyone (not just vegans), vitamin D is frequently ignored. More interestingly, vitamin K2 has never before been mentioned in vegan literature. I've seen many raw vegan children *not grow*, have severe cavities and tooth rot and struggle with profound mental development problems even while just in the breastfeeding stage because the mothers have been deficient in vitamins D and K2.

I've been researching the true health of raw vegan children for years. Despite my searching, I haven't found one lifelong raw vegan unsupplemented child past the age of breastfeeding who is healthy in all aspects. Not supplementing your child when removing all animal products is dangerous and irresponsible and it could lead to lifelong problems for your child.

If you've previously been misled by raw vegan literature you may now find your child in a state of deficiency. Don't panic and don't feel guilty, but please take action now. If your child is too thin, frail, birdlike, short, has a strange head shape, seems vacant, has slow development, or doesn't seem "quite right" please seek the help of a raw-friendly nutritionist to correct the deficiencies with higher levels of supplements and maybe animal produce.

A healthy raw vegan child should be the correct height, have a broad face, and be developing at the same rate as all other children. Obviously fluctuations occur, which is why it can help to ask impartial others if your child seems OK to you.

The ones to Watch

Here's a comprehensive list of all the nutrients that you need to keep an eye out for when feeding your child a raw vegan diet.

Vitamin D

This is a fat-soluble vitamin which can be stored in the body for about six months if you have enough. Small amounts of vitamin D can be found in green leafy vegetables, especially nettles. However, the prime food sources of this vitamin are egg yolk and fish. An egg only supplies 6% of the RDA and fish doesn't do much better. The only significant dietary source of vitamin D is cod liver oil, a dosage of which supplies around 350% of the RDA. However, this has been linked to vitamin A toxicity. Also, cod liver oil may contain undesirable levels of mercury and other heavy metals.

Vitamin D is found in fortified vegan margarines and soya drinks, but these aren't raw. Vitamin D is synthesised via the skin from the sun.

Vitamin D comes in two forms within supplements. The most common is D3 (cholecalciferol) which is usually from the lanolin of sheep's wool. This isn't acceptable for most ethical vegans. Vitamin D2 (ergocalciferol) is synthesised, so quite unnatural and isn't acceptable to those wanting to eat naturally. It's also slightly less efficient than vitamin D3. However, the inclusion of vitamin D is so important, you simply have to make a choice if your food or sun sources are scarce. In the UK, you can easily obtain free vitamin D supplements via your GP from pregnancy onwards if you are at all concerned.

Importance

We need vitamin D for bone growth: it's vital that young children have enough of it. A deficiency in vitamin D can lead to rickets and deformed bones. Common early symptoms of rickets include restlessness, profuse sweating, lack of muscle tone in the limbs and abdomen, and delay in learning to sit, crawl and walk. Vitamin D deficiency may also cause osteoporosis, which increases the chance of bones fracturing. In adults, vitamin D deficiency can lead to osteomalacia (progressive loss of calcium and phosphorus from the bones). All pregnant and breastfeeding mothers need to be vigilant about this vitamin as deficiency can affect both them and their child. The liver provides the chief storage tissue for vitamins A, D and K.

Bearing all this in mind, vegans are at a slightly higher risk of vitamin D deficiency because of the almost complete lack of dietary vitamin D. However, the risk to the omnivorous population (via dietary insufficiency) is still high. This is why vegans, vegetarians and omnivores look to supplement and fortify with vitamin D or make a real effort to sunbathe enough to get it via sunlight.

It's natural for us to live in a sunny climate where vitamin D is abundant through high sun exposure. We are tropical creatures living in temperate zones. For mothers in temperate zones vitamin D is often present at such a low level that the breastfed baby doesn't get enough. When her natural stores are depleted, there is no vitamin D available for healthy growth.

If you're going to bring your child up as cooked or raw vegan in the UK you must supplement with vitamin D somehow, from the word go. If you're breastfeeding in the summer, and you're getting adequate sun exposure, then a year without artificial supplementation is OK as you'll gain and store lots of vitamin D from the sun which will be passed on to your child through your milk.

If you wish to take supplements and breastfeed your unsupplemented child, you must take in at least 2,000 IU of vitamin D per day yourself. This will create normal levels of vitamin D in the child. You may wish to take in more so your child has the opportunity to take in more than the "normal" amount. Though there has never been a death due to vitamin D supplementation overdose (there has been due to industrial accidents), be aware that excessive doses can lead to toxicity.

If you don't want to supplement yourself while breastfeeding you must ensure that you have enough exposure to the sunshine. If you are not breastfeeding and don't want to supplement your child, you must ensure she has sufficient exposure to the sunshine without burning her.

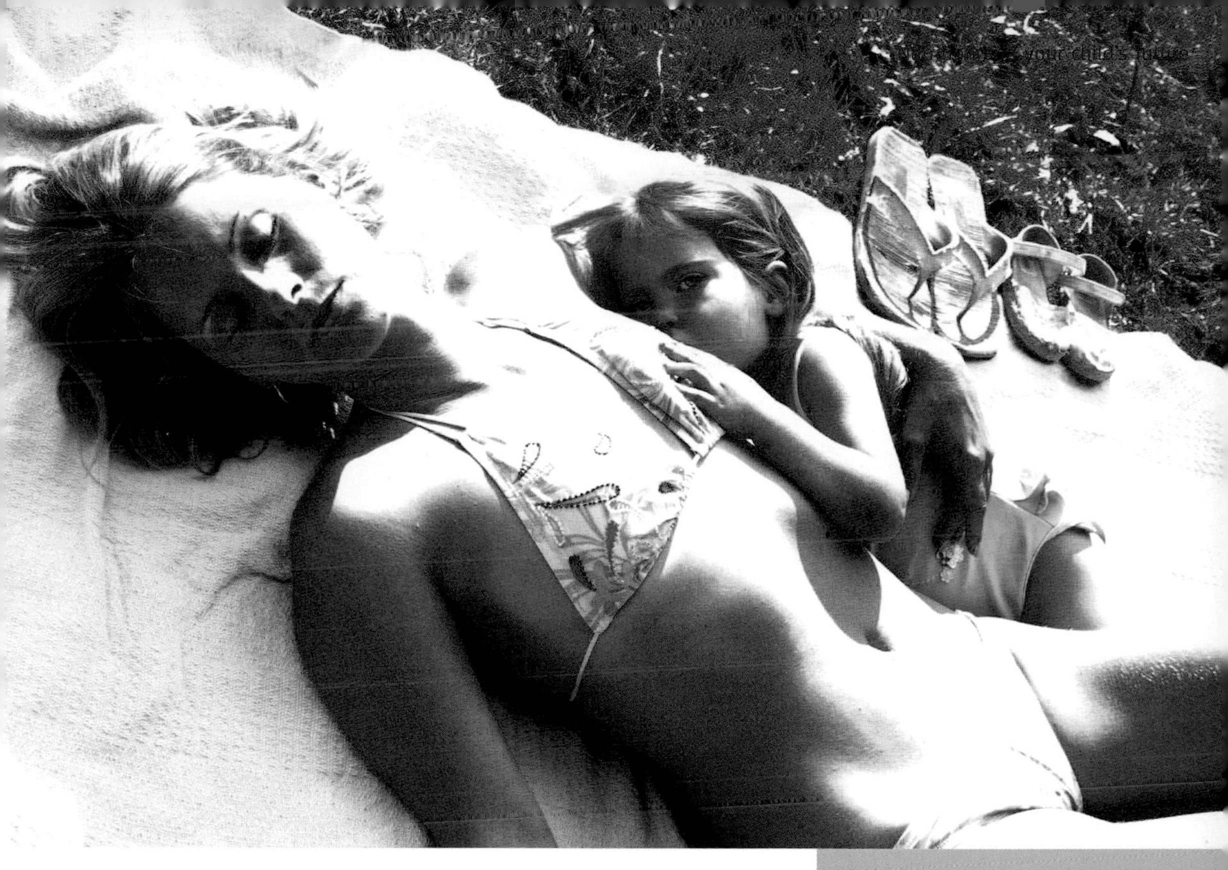

If your child is eating cooked vegan foods that are fortified with vitamin D or if he's getting lots of regular sun exposure, he may be OK. However, I wouldn't take that risk for my child because of the irreversible deformities caused.

Though many people are scared of sunbathing these days, new information by researchers at the Moores Cancer Center, USA states that raised levels of vitamin D (from sunbathing) prevents more breast, ovary and colon cancers than it causes skin cancers. (Science Daily, May 2006).

How to get enough

The adult RDA for vitamin D is just 400 IU. The RDA for small children is double that (depending on which health authority you reference) due to their rate of bone growth. This is the minimum amount your child needs to prevent rickets. She actually needs more than this for healthy growth, and cannot overdose if you double or triple this amount. Experts such as Professor Robert Heaney say that adults should take at least 2000 IU as a supplement on top of food and sunlight exposure.

Sunshine exposure guidelines

It's generally agreed that we need moderate sun exposure for vitamin D synthesis. Sunscreens with UV protection directly affect vitamin D production, and for that reason I've never used them on Evie. Instead

I ensure she gets naked when it's sunny, outside of the 11am-3pm sunshine, for about an hour. If we're out for longer than that she wears a long-sleeved cool top and a floppy hat. Having said that, raw people don't burn so readily as people who eat cooked food. Sometimes Evie has had much more sun exposure than recommended and has never burned.

From April to September in the UK, get naked. If you're not naked you need to sunbathe longer. For each 5% of body surface exposed, the skin can make about 100-200 IU of vitamin D in a single session.

When naked, adults can produce about 20,000-30,000 IU of vitamin D on a bright summer's day in one high-sun sunbathing session (low sun doesn't work).

In the UK, up to 34% of young Asian children are vitamin D deficient, compared to 2% of white children. This is why you need to take your skin type into consideration. The time of one session varies with skin colour:

- White skin 10-20 minutes
- Black skin 120 minutes or more
- Asian/mixed skin is somewhere in between, depending on colour

If you and your child sunbathe enough for your skin colour, you don't need to supplement in the winter. However, if you are pregnant or breastfeeding a child, or if your child has minimal sun exposure please consider supplementing.

Vitamin B12

Vitamin B12 is classed as a water-soluble vitamin. Bacterial enzymes within our colon produce vitamin B12 but we can't absorb it at that site—we absorb it in the small intestine. This means it's highly unlikely that we can use the vitamin B12 that's created inside us, unless we eat poo! We therefore have to look to food sources or supplements to get enough vitamin B12. It can be found in small (not the RDA) amounts in seaweed, algae, and maca. Be aware that some algaes have B12 analogues, which compete for real B12 absorption. Some yeast extracts, soya milks and other cooked vegan foods are fortified with vitamin B12. It is in dairy produce, eggs, and all other animal foods in reasonable to high amounts.

Importance

Vitamin B12 deficiency can seriously damage your child's health. Children need vitamin B12 for healthy red blood cells, a good nervous system and good growth and development. Dietary-related vitamin B12 deficiency is rare, but raw vegans should take extra care because our diet excludes the foods that provide this vitamin.

Symptoms of deficiency include colour blindness, light-headedness, confusion, speech delay, depression, tinnitus, neuropathy, poor concentration and forgetfulness. There may also be loss of appetite, diarrhoea and weight loss.

Those with vitamin B12 deficiency anaemia (pernicious anaemia) can suffer breathlessness, tiredness, dizziness, a rapid and weak pulse rate, palpitations, headaches and pale skin. If left untreated, pernicious anaemia can become life-threatening.

Parasites or certain bacteria that interfere with absorption in the small intestine can also cause poor absorption of vitamin B12.

How to get enough

The best and most reassuring way for vegans to prevent vitamin B12 deficiency is via supplementation. You don't need much, either:

- 0 to 6 months 0.3 µg per day
- 7 to 12 months 0.4 µg per day
- 1 to 3 yrs 0.5 µg per day
- 4 to 6 yrs 0.8 µg per day
- 7 to 10 yrs 1.0 µg per day
- 11 to 14 yrs 1.2 µg per day
- 15 + yrs 1.5 µg per day
- Breastfeeding women 2.0 µg per day

Vitamin B12 stores well in the body, so you can take a larger supplement once a week if you want to. Most vitamin B12 supplements contain several times the RDA of vitamin B12. However, the amount that is absorbed is very low. This means you may still be at risk of deficiency even when it looks like you're taking enough. There are several vitamin B12 sprays available, which use nanotechnology to deliver very high doses sublingually. The vitamin goes straight into the bloodstream, ensuring you absorb plenty. This is my preferred supplement, and it's also what I give Evie. She doesn't like the spraying action, so I mix it in water and use a syringe to feed her.

Vitamin K1 and K2

Dr Weston Price was a pioneering ethnographic-nutritionist. In the 1930s he discovered "a new vitamin-like activator" that seemed to play a critical role in growth, development, the utilisation of minerals and also in the prevention of tooth cavities. He also related its importance to healthy reproductive organs, the brain and the heart. He called this substance activator X. It has since been classed as vitamin K.

Vitamin K is a fat-soluble vitamin which is only stored in the body for a short time. It exists in two forms: K1 and K2. Vitamin K1 is easy to find in algaes, grasses and green leafy vegetables. Therefore it's normally abundant in a raw vegan diet.

Vitamin K2 is abundant in egg yolk, orange-coloured butter made from grass-fed ruminants such as cows and goats, organ meat and also in some cheeses. In the vegetable kingdom vitamin K2 is only found in fermented foods such as natto (fermented soya beans) and sauerkraut (fermented cabbage).

Vitamin K2 is converted from vitamin K1 by bacteria in the intestines. Humans do this much less effectively than ruminants, and so we can't convert as much as we need. To further complicate this, vitamin K2 MK-4 is the most common form, yet there are others such as MK-7, which is still highly bio-available.

100g of natto contains 1103mcg of vitamin K2 (MK-7), hard cheese contains about 76mcg (mostly MK-7), egg yolk contains 32mcg (mostly MK-4), butter contains 15mcg (MK-4), sauerkraut contains 4mcg (mostly MK-7) and whole milk contains 1mcg (MK-4). Though natto contains a lot of vitamin K2, it's hard to find, and most people are repulsed by its taste.

Importance

In his book, *Nutritional And Physical Degeneration*, Price outlined the synergistic link between vitamins A, D and K2. Vitamins A and D are critical in the production of important proteins, and vitamin K2 is required to activate these proteins once they are made. For example, the protein osteocalcin is critical to mineral deposition in our teeth and bones. It's produced in the presence of vitamins A and D, but requires vitamin K2 to perform its function. Higher vitamin K intake seems to correspond to greater bone density. To further illustrate the perfection of nature it's worth noting that vitamin K2 also protects against vitamin D toxicity.

Without enough vitamin K2, cavities in the teeth, stunted growth and facial deformities can occur, as can gastro-intestinal bleeding, easy bruising and other haemophiliac-type symptoms. If your raw vegan child is too light and birdlike, too small, has sunken cheeks, a pinched nose or has bad teeth, then you need to take immediate action to supplement his diet or alter it to include sufficient humanely sourced animal by-products. When supplementing a child to correct deficiencies, I strongly recommend you work with a nutritionist or switched-on dietician.

A note to women: vitamin K has been used in the treatment of heavy menstrual bleeding, and is occasionally used alongside vitamin C to treat morning sickness.

A few newborns are at risk of vitamin K deficiency. This is because their digestive tracts contain no vitamin K-producing bacteria. I chose not to have Evie supplemented with vitamin K at birth because I read about risks associated with it. Discuss this with your midwife if you are concerned.

Prolonged use of antibiotics, eating foods containing hydrogenated vegetable oil and several gastro-intestinal diseases can decrease the absorption of vitamin K. A vegan diet that lacks any vitamin K2 supplementation may also result in vitamin K2 deficiency.

How to get enough

We need constant intakes of vitamin K1 and vitamin K2 at least every few days to remain healthy because we don't store it for very long in our bodies.

There is no RDA for vitamin K2, yet I worked out a 5 year old would need about 55mcg per day.

I recommend all raw vegan children drink a pint of green juice a day, and eat algae very often. There will be some vitamin K2 conversion from these foods. However, it won't be enough for a growing child, so I thoroughly recommend daily supplementation, too.

Mercola's vitamin K2 (MK-7) and Ortho-Bone Vegan (MK-4) are both excellent vegan vitamin K2 sources. One serving of twelve capsules of Ortho-Bone Vegan offers 250mcg, but you couldn't get that into a child! Your child can get enough vitamin K2 from taking around four capsules mixed into drinks daily. Mercola's supplement contains

100mcg in one very small capsule, which can be opened and mixed into savoury food.

A pregnant or breastfeeding woman should have about 90mcg a day, but I would double that, because it's so important for your child's growth.

There is no known toxicity associated with high doses of vitamin K1, vitamin K2 and their derivatives. High intake of vitamin K is not recommended for individuals taking anticoagulant medications such as Warfarin.

DHA and EPA

DHA is docosahexaenoic acid and EPA is eicosapentaenoic acid — big words with big functions. They both come from omega 3 fat, which is found in cold water fish and algae along with seed oils. These polyunsaturated long-chain fats play a vital role in our bodies.

Importance

DHA is a building block for brain and retina tissue. It helps the formation of neural transmitters, which is important for brain function. EPA and DHA are converted into hormone-like substances called prostaglandins, which regulate cell activity and help cardiovascular function.

Sufficient DHA is essential for foetal development, early infancy, and old age. High concentrations of DHA are found in the brain (about 25% of all brain fat is DHA). DHA content increases 300-500% in an infant's brain during the last trimester of pregnancy. The University of Alberta, Canada confirmed in a study that DHA in formula milk (from algae) resulted in enhanced growth. I wholeheartedly recommend that all pregnant women supplement with DHA, regardless of their diet. To ensure optimal brain development, continue supplementation via breastfeeding until your child is at least two years of age.

EPA is considered by some UK health professionals such as Patrick Holford and Dale Pinnock as being the single most vital nutrient in the functioning of the brain and nerve stimulation. It has been successfully used (with the DHA absent) to help treat patients suffering from depression and schizophrenia. EPA is also very beneficial for the daily functioning of the brain.

EPA and DHA act as a source of energy. This energy insulates the body against heat loss, prevents skin from drying and flaking, and cushions tissues and organs.

How to get enough

Taking 300mg of DHA throughout your life should cover initial brain growth as well as old age degeneration. However, when pregnant or breastfeeding, I'd feel happier if raw vegan mums were taking 1000mg a day. I recommend you also supplement your child directly as soon as she is eating food with 300mg of DHA a day.

In my view the best vegan DHA supplement is O-Mega-Zen-3, which contains 300mg of DHA per capsule. Around 10% of the DHA is converted into EPA in the body, which means you get about 30mg of EPA in each capsule, though it's not listed. V-Pure contains both DHA and EPA but the capsules aren't as concentrated, each capsule containing just 90mg of DHA and 25mg of EPA. I'm not 100% happy about the processing of these products, as solvents may be used, but they are still the best vegan options available at the moment.

Some supplements use fish oil as a source of DHA, but the fish themselves get their DHA directly from algae — and so do both O-Mega-Zen-3 and V-Pure. As well as being more ethical than fish oil there is no risk of heavy metal or PCB poisoning with these products — as there can be with some fish-derived DHA and EPA. Algae is also great for the environment: for each tonne of algae grown, over two tonnes of carbon dioxide are removed from the atmosphere.

Another great source of DHA and EPA is marine phytoplankton. It is also rich in chlorophyll and trace minerals. It is a nutrient-dense whole food and you can buy it in powdered form.

Salba (salvia hispanica) is another good source of omega 3 and is also rich in fibre, magnesium and antioxidants. Ground into a fine flour it can be mixed with juice for an EFA boost, or used in a number of delicious and varied dishes. Chia is very similar to Salba, though at the time of writing both are classed as novel foods in the UK and so you need to buy them from the Internet.

Though flaxseed oil is high in the omega 3 fatty acid ALA (alphalinoic acid), you'd need to take in about 11 grams of flaxseed oil to make 1 gram of EPA. In addition, allergic anaphylactic reactions have been reported with flaxseed and flaxseed oil ingestion. This is why I suggest directly supplementing with the long chain fatty acids.

As we get older our bodies form less DHA and EPA, which may reduce mental focus and cognitive function. This is why it's useful to supplement more at this time. It has been suggested by the National Institute on Aging in the USA and others that taking EPA and DHA may help with mental abnormalities, such as Alzheimer's Disease and Dementia.

If you are deficient in DHA your body can convert EPA into DHA, as well as converting DHA into EPA, though this process is less efficient.

Iron

Iron is a mineral available as haeme and non-haeme forms. Haeme iron is found in meat, poultry and fish products and non-haeme iron is found in plant foods and eggs. Your body absorbs four times as much haeme iron as non-haeme iron, which is why the vegetarian and vegan RDA is different to the omnivore RDA.

Importance

Low iron levels over a long period of time can eventually suppress haemoglobin production. This is iron-deficiency anaemia, typically diagnosed by counting the number of red blood cells in a sample and looking at their sizes.

Iron deficiency is one of the most common nutrient deficiencies in our society. There is a higher risk of iron deficiency during these four periods of life: 6 months to 4 years, adolescence, during the female reproductive time, and during pregnancy. During infancy iron-deficiency anaemia can permanently affect brain development, and in early childhood iron deficiency interferes with growth, weight gain and behavioural development. This is why you need to take care that this mineral is present and absorbed in your growing child.

Adults with mild iron deficiency experience no obvious problems other than vague symptoms of tiredness, headache, irritability, or depression. Signs and symptoms of iron-deficiency anaemia include pale skin, brittle fingernails, tiredness, weakness, apathy, breathlessness especially on physical exertion, giddiness, palpitations, reduced immune function, inadequate temperature regulation, loss of appetite, headache, behavioural disturbances and reduced intellectual performance. The fatigue is caused by insufficient synthesis of red blood cells and cytochromes. These symptoms are similar to those of other health problems and diseases, making it very difficult to self-diagnose anaemia.

Though you may hear that meat is a great source of iron, it is just a marketing claim. Prime beef contains just 2-3% of absorbable iron — no more than spinach. Around 80% of toddlers develop anaemia, which suggests that iron deficiency isn't limited to vegans. Studies show that the iron status of vegans is usually normal, and iron deficiency is no more common than in the general population. Iron is present in many foods — it's just sometimes harder to absorb. It's now commonly recommended that vegetarians and vegans eat twice the RDA of iron to ensure the uptake is sufficient.

Teenage girls need to take more iron because of the menstrual changes they go through. However, naturally raised teenage girls shouldn't get the haemorrhaging that standard western teenage girls do, so their need wouldn't be as high. Use your judgement here, as all girls will be different.

When pregnant, your needs are also higher than normal. This is partly due to the baby's needs and also due to your own body building up iron levels to get you through childbirth.

Iron toxicity can be serious, so you need to be careful when supplementing. There's a genetic disorder called Haemochromatosis, where people absorb more iron than normal. This can lead to organ damage through high iron storage levels. Meat-based (haeme) iron poses the greatest risk for people with this disorder.

Iron is a pro-oxidant. It promotes the oxidative damage that is linked to many chronic diseases. In some studies, excess iron stores (and intakes) have been linked to increased risk of heart disease and certain forms of cancer, particularly colo-rectal cancer. Other studies have shown that lower iron stores may reduce the risk of diabetes through enhancing insulin sensitivity.

How to get enough

The RDA for iron has increased in recent years as health professionals realise how important this mineral is and how difficult it is for people to assimilate it.

The Canadian standard RDA for iron is slightly higher than the UK's so I go by that, to be safe:

- 0 to 6 months 0.27mg per day (via breastmilk only)
- 7 to 12 months 11 mg per day (via breastmilk and food)
- 1 to 3 years 7mg per day (via breastmilk and food)
- 4 to 8 years 10mg per day
- 9 to 13 years 8mg per day
- 14 to 18 years 11mg (m) 18mg (f) per day
- 19 to 30 years 8mg (m) 18mg (f) per day
- 31 to 50 years 8mg (m) 18mg (f) per day
- 51 to 70 years 8mg (m) 8mg (f) per day
- Pregnancy 27mg (f) per day
- Breastfeeding 10mg (f) per day (I'm guessing this is lower than a normal female because of the absence of menstruation, though I menstruated throughout my breastfeeding career, so again use your judgement.)

Of haeme iron, your body will absorb about 23%. Of non-haeme iron, you'll absorb about 3-5%. To make it more complicated, non-haeme iron absorption amounts can be increased or decreased according to

what you eat alongside the iron. Some components in tea and coffee, oxalates in spinach, or phytates in whole grains and nuts, can limit the amount of non-haeme iron your body can absorb. Fermentation, germination, sprouting and even soaking of these products can improve iron absorption. Taking iron with foods rich in vitamin C can increase non-haeme iron uptake.

Here are my top raw foods containing an abundance of non-haeme iron. Most of these foods are also naturally high in vitamin C because nature loves us and wants us to get iron from plants. Feel free to mix these foods with other foods rich in vitamin C to ensure maximum absorption.

- Wheatgrass Juice 56mg of iron per 100g (14mg in a 25g serving)
- Spirulina 28.5mg/100g (3mg in a 10g serving)
- Amaranth 15mg/100g (100g is a normal serving)
- Pistachios 14mg/100g (7mg in a 50g serving)
- Pumpkin seeds 11.2mg/100g (5.5mg in a 50g serving)
- Sesame seeds 10.4mg/100g (3mg in a 30g serving)
- Quinoa 9.3mg/100g (15g in a 150g serving)
- Sundried tomatoes 9.09mg/100g (4.5 in a 50g serving)
- Barley miso 8.6mg/100g (2.5mg in a 30g serving)
- Goji berries 8.42mg/100g (2.5mg in a 30g serving)
- Broad beans 6.67mg/100g (100g is a normal serving)
- Sunflower seeds 6.8mg/100g (2mg in a 30g serving)
- Parsley 6.2 mg/100g (0.6g in a 10g serving)
- Apricots 4.1mg/100g (100g is a normal serving)
- Figs 4.2mg/100g (100g is a normal serving)

It's also worth mentioning that a teaspoon of Seagreens has the iron of a plate of broccoli and the calcium of half a cup of milk.

When pregnant and breastfeeding, I recommend long-term use of ionic iron, which is 99.9% absorbable. When your child starts drinking other drinks you can add small amounts of this supplement to those drinks. I give Evie about four teaspoons a day in her coconut water but she also likes to drink it straight. This allows iron stores to build up in her body and remain stable. I consider ionic iron to be the best supplemental iron because of its absorption rate. Ionic minerals have molecule clusters that are small enough to be fully utilised by the body. Please remember that using iron supplementation inappropriately could lead to an oxidant effect on the body, and so you must not experiment with huge doses of iron.

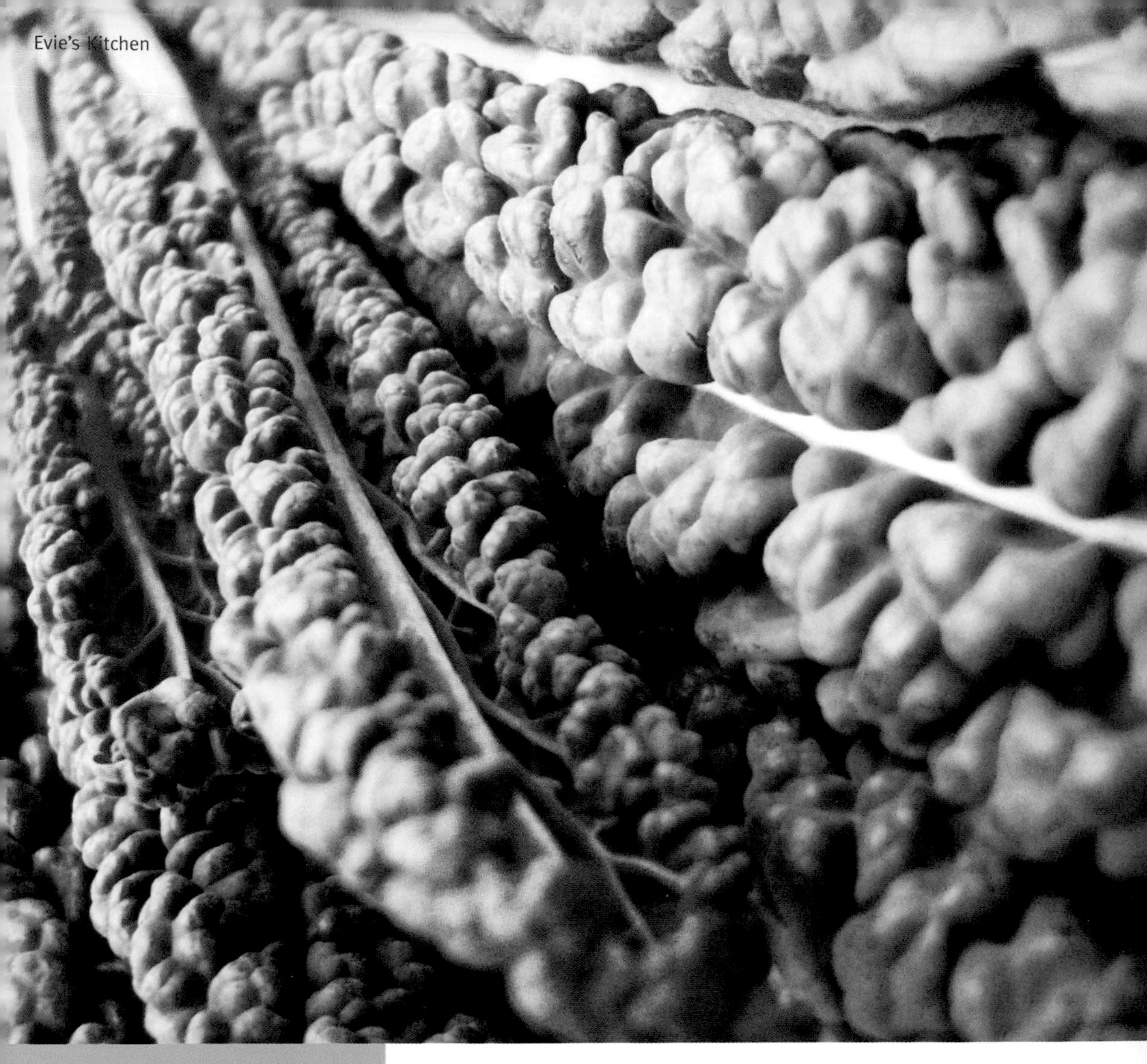

Calcium

Calcium is a major mineral, which is essential for healthy bones and teeth. It is in most foods, and is abundant in broccoli, sesame seeds, figs and dairy products. Though it's in most foods, I've listed it here because we need such a large amount of it.

Importance

Calcium is essential for the good development and long-term health of bones and teeth. It needs to be consumed constantly otherwise we begin to draw it from our bones and they weaken. Eating a diet low in bioavailable calcium long-term can lead to osteoporosis, a condition in which the bone deteriorates and fractures can occur much more easily.

It is possible to consume too much calcium and end up with hypercalcaemia (excessively high levels of calcium in the blood) or calcium deposits in the tissues. Hypercalcaemia is normally only caused by an overactive parathyroid gland. Raised calcium levels in the blood can lead to impaired kidney function and decreased absorption of other minerals. If it gets really bad it can lead to nausea, vomiting, seizures and even coma. Vitamin D is intrinsically linked to calcium and is needed to regulate calcium levels in the blood.

How to get enough

Dietary calcium requirements depend in part upon whether the body is growing or making new bone or milk. Requirements are therefore greatest during childhood, adolescence, pregnancy, and breastfeeding. The recommended daily intake of elemental (totally absorbable) calcium varies accordingly.

There is about 10mg of calcium in every 30ml of human milk. Some children tend to guzzle almost constantly; others are a bit more sporadic. From seven to twelve months, the adequate intake of calcium is determined to be 270mg per day. If your 12-month-old is getting nearly 900ml of breast milk a day, she's certainly getting enough calcium. Things change fast though, and between the ages of one and three your child will need 500mg every day. Here's a table of the calcium your child needs over time:

- 210mg for ages 1-6 months
- 270mg for ages 6-12 months
- 500mg for children 1–3 years
- 1,200mg for ages 11–24 years
- 800mg for individuals over 24 years of age
- Pregnant women need about 1,200mg
- Many experts believe that elderly persons should take as much as 1,500 mg to help prevent osteoporosis.

Dairy products such as milk and cheese are the best-known source of calcium. However, I look for healthier and more ecstatic ways of consuming calcium. Fortunately, many vegan sources of calcium exist. Here's my list of favourite calcium-rich foods.

- Light tahini 680mg of calcium per 100g (270mg in a 40g serving)
- Almonds 250mg/100g (75mg in a 30g serving)
- Figs 250mg/100g (100g is a normal serving)
- Nori 236mg/100g (36mg in a 15g serving)
- Dandelion leaf 187mg/100g (28mg in a 15g serving)
- Kale 180mg/100g (90mg in a 50g serving)

- Parsley 138mg/100g (14mg in a 10g serving)
- Watercress 136mg/100g (68mg in a 50g serving)
- Kelp 133mg/100g (7mg in a 5g serving)
- Pak choi 105mg/100g (63mg in a 60g serving)
- Quinoa 85mg/100g (127mg in a 150g serving)
- Tamari 82mg/100g (4mg in a 5g serving)
- Okra 81mg/100g (64mg in a 80g serving)
- Broccoli 77mg/100g (100g is a normal serving)
- Butternut squash 70mg/100g (100g is a normal serving)

A child needs 800mg a day of totally bio-available calcium. This is occasionally difficult to achieve on a raw vegan diet. The answer has to be copious amounts of green juices, preferably about a pint a day, which will provide your child with a bounty of trace minerals, protein, enzymes and vitamins. I realise this is not always possible, and not 100% of the calcium in the juice will be absorbed. This is why I recommend the Ortho-Bone Vegan supplement, sprinkled into food. This supplement also provides enough magnesium, silica and other bone-health minerals in the correct ratio to calcium.

Here's an example of how you can integrate your child's calcium needs into his day. Take into consideration that most foods contain some calcium, so this is not the full daily intake:

Light tahini	40g	270mg
Nori	15g	36mg
Figs	100g	250mg
Almonds	30g	75mg
Butternut squash	100g	70mg
Total		**701mg**

Topping up our calcium levels is easy, delicious and fun. Look below for an example of a high calcium juice. I get Evie drinking green juice as often as possible. It really is the best way a vegan raw child will reach her RDA in calcium. Apples and carrots help to sweeten it up.

Kale	85g	150mg
Broccoli	80g	60mg
Parsley	30g	40mg
Watercress	30g	40mg
Total		**290mg**

With a complete total of nearly 1000mg a day, this example shows that a raw vegan diet can provide enough calcium alongside other important minerals, especially when green juices are given daily.

A child laughs 400 times a day, and the average woman laughs only 15 times a day. Let's start the laughter revolution now!

Choline

Choline is an organic compound, classified as an essential nutrient and usually grouped within the vitamin B complex. This natural nutrient is found in fats and the lipids that make up cell walls. It plays a crucial role in neurotransmitter function. Now for the inconvenient truth for raw vegans: 99% of choline exists within the animal kingdom. It's in their eggs, their offal and their meat.

Importance

Choline appears to play a key role in brain development, and among other things it appears to stimulate cell division in the developing brain.

Deficiency symptoms generally include liver damage and an abundance of fat in and around the liver. It can lead to nerve degeneration, senile dementia, high blood cholesterol and liver cancer.

Choline is important for nerve structure and function. Uptake of choline into the brain decreases with age. And this change may contribute to a type of dementia.

How to get enough

Some dark leafy vegetables do contain choline. However, to ensure your child is getting enough, a supplement won't go amiss. Choline citrate appears to be the most absorbable but is currently only available from the USA. However, lecithin from soya contains a lot of choline. Look out for high-PC versions of lecithin. There is no set RDA for choline, but it's been suggested that 1000-1500mg a day would be optimal. I give Evie Udo's Choice oil, which contains choline and lecithin. I also give her soya lecithin granules, mixed into her food.

Further information

Biological Transmutations — Louis C Kervran. Louis discovered that certain elemental changes exist in living things which can stabilise life. This book answers many nutritional questions.

Lorena Bull, Registered Dietician and Certified Lactation Expert (RD and CLE). She has over 25 years' experience in vegetarian, vegan and raw food diets. Based in the USA, Lorena does consultations worldwide. She is particularly interested in ensuring young raw and vegan children are nutritionally complete.
LorenaBullRD@Gmail.com, myspace.com/LorenaBullRD

Breastfeeding

Breastfeeding is the single most important nutritional gift you can give your child. My very good friend and author of *The Drinks Are On Me*, Veronika Robinson, rocked the world in 2006 when she took part in the Channel Four documentary *Extraordinary Breastfeeding*. To some viewers Veronika was a freak. Yet to many others, including me, Veronika was and continues to be a shining divine beam of light who gave up a huge amount of privacy for the benefit of the masses.

Our viewpoints are extremely similar, and I urge you to read her book. It's fun and factual. Yes, it's factual. Veronika isn't some weird hippy woman who can't let her children grow up. In many other societies she'd be revered as the goddess she actually is. Yet most people in the UK and the USA don't recognise what's real and good for children any more because of unnatural cultural programming.

Breastfed children catch fewer "colds", don't have a constantly runny nose, and don't display other symptoms of toxicity.

Reasons to be milky

There is no reason why anyone with functioning breasts and a healthy child should choose to bottle-feed. Given the full facts, and in a supportive environment, it's very easy and lovely to do. We need to nurture a culture where real mothering is respected and revered, regardless of the clever marketing of formula companies.

Yes, there are some mothers who can't breastfeed, and my heart really goes out to them. But there are many other mothers who just aren't aware how utterly important breastfeeding is to their child, so they don't even try. I feel this is one of the most important subjects in human history.

Bottle-feeding is prevalent, more accepted than breastfeeding in public, and seen as a lifestyle choice. It's not a case of choice, as the baby doesn't have a choice. Babies just want the right amount of love and nutrients so they can grow happily and healthily. Any mother who thinks that a career, her partner and endless parties are more important than the correct nourishment of her child may need to look more closely at her priorities.

At the time of writing, the law in the UK is being altered: it's now illegal to move on or disturb a breastfeeding mother in public. However, when that child turns six months, the mother could be prosecuted for indecent exposure. It's strange that we have a law protecting and then suddenly preventing something that's right and natural, but at least women with small babies can no longer be commanded to breastfeed in public toilets.

Evie and I have the best social life ever. She often comes with me to parties as she's accepted as part of me. I used to breastfeed her whenever she wanted it. I've breastfed her on the floor of a shop when she fell over and needed her "booboo". That one even attracted a comment: "Wow" said an elderly man, "you're amazing, doing that here. Well done". I breastfed Evie in public right up until her fourth birthday, and nobody acted negatively towards me. "Discreet" breastfeeding is a farce: there's nothing wrong with feeding your child the food it was designed to eat, no matter what the law says.

Be a pioneer and get your boobs out in public, you divine breastfeeding goddess, you! Self-assured breastfeeding mothers only attract positive comments from others, no matter what age their child is.

When you get it right, breastfeeding a child is so relaxing. You get to lie down. There are no bottles to clean. The milk's always there, warm and ready. It's free! Human breastmilk, from a woman who has taken care with her nutrition, is perfect for human children. It supplies everything your baby needs. Immediately.

Detoxing before pregnancy and while breastfeeding

People who eat non-organic meat have more toxins in their bodies than vegans or vegetarians, since these animals eat lots of non-organic food and the chemicals are concentrated in their meat. They are also injected with poisons known as drugs: when people eat this meat they too are bombarded with chemicals.

It's best to detox yourself and the potential father before becoming pregnant whenever possible. However, if you don't manage this, your baby is still better off with your milk than formula milk.

You can choose right now, with your baby, to make a difference to our baby-feeding culture.

"Artificial baby milks are more contaminated than breastmilk, in different ways. They have been found to contain phthalates, bisphenol A, aluminium and heavy metals, GM ingredients, phytoestrogens and spore bacteria. Any increase in artificial feeding would result in greater contamination of the environment". — *Babymilkaction.org*

You can easily follow the advice I give in my book *Detox Your World*:

We all know that breast is best when feeding your baby. Nutrients aside, feel-good hormones found in breast milk but not in formula milk make for a contented child. However, toxins are powerful and will get into breast milk if they're floating around the body looking for a way out.

Luckily, women can minimise the pesticides in their breast milk very easily. The breast milk of vegetarians (and vegans even more so) shows lower levels of the pesticides DDT, chlordane, heptachlor and dieldrin, and industrial compounds or by-products such as polychlorinated biphenyls (PCBs) and polychlorinated dibenzodiozins. Virginia Messina and Mark Messina explain this all in the Dietitian's Guide to Vegetarian Diets. *This information confirms many other studies:*

- *Over twenty years ago the breast milk of many vegans was analysed. The levels of 17 chemicals were markedly lower than in non-vegans.*
- *A few studies have linked frequent consumption of meat, dairy and fish to breast milk contamination.*
- *In the 1970s a study revealed that pesticide levels were far lower in the breast milk of vegetarian women.*

The above results should make everyone think twice about eating animal products. I've always said that if I wasn't a vegan for ethical reasons, I'd certainly be one for health reasons.

Because plant foods don't store pesticides in the way animals do, they are much safer to eat even if they have been sprayed. This means that weight for weight, non-organic fruit will have much lower amounts of pesticides than animal flesh or milk.

So if you're breastfeeding or even planning a baby, take great care to ensure that most if not all of your diet is organic and plant-based. This way you won't be passing on such high levels of toxins to your precious little one. And even if you're already breastfeeding, please don't switch to formula as you still have superior nutrients and feel-good hormones that bottled milk can't match.

I was about to become a mother and that is about as genius as it gets. The appearance of my colostrum quickly altered me from being an unsure thirtysomething to a wise and connected mother-to-be.

It's really sensible to embark on a cleanse six months before conceiving. In addition, add a good multi-vitamin and mineral supplement (containing folic acid), DHA, and get any toxic mercury (amalgam) fillings out. Eating as much organic food as possible is really important. Eating wild food is even better. Read *Detox Your World* for more information on which foods are the worst offenders if not organic, and which ones aren't so bad. Knowing this information really helps when you just can't eat 100% organic food. The book also contains several detox plans to fit in with your specific lifestyle.

Dozens of studies pooled together by Cancer Research UK have shown a significant decrease in ovarian and breast cancer in mothers who breastfeed long term. Doing a pre-pregnancy detox and then breastfeeding is beneficial to our children and us.

If you are already breastfeeding and this information has scared you, there is something you can do to lower the levels of toxins as you continue to breastfeed. Look for oxygen supplements and zeolites. Oxygenate or safely ozonate your air, get fresh air when you can, wear the purest clothes possible, eat more organic food, and use toxin-free toiletries and housecleaning products. Oxygen is a scavenger of pathogens. It will find and metabolise (destroy) toxins that are floating around in your bloodstream. You have to be consistent with oxygen therapies and other detox methods, though. Your toxins have built up over decades; just getting a weekend of fresh air isn't enough.

Nature's first starter

Colostrum comes from the nipples before breastmilk, often months before birth. It's thick and sticky, yellow in colour. Colostrum acts as a laxative to aid the removal of meconium from the baby's gut. Meconium is the baby's first poos, and it's like liquid tar. Some people who have detoxed a lot claim to have no or little meconium in their baby's first poos. Evie only had a small amount of meconium.

Colostrum contains huge amounts of immune-boosting antibodies, proteins, peptides and transfer factor. Transfer factor appears to transfer information to major immune cells about specific pathogens. The cells then destroy these pathogens if they are ever encountered. As your newborn suckles, all of these nutrients are absorbed through the baby's permeable intestines. After about six hours, the baby's gut seals up and the colostrum becomes sweet with sugar. Mucus begins to line your baby's intestines and the sugar feeds the microflora. The microflora then stick to the mucus. This is how babies get a fully functioning immume system.

I got my colostrum when around five months pregnant. I was overjoyed at my body being able to produce something so soon into my pregnancy that boosts the immunity of my child. I tasted it, photographed it and videoed it. What a wonderfully clever body.

Some people are concerned that if they are still breastfeeding when pregnant, there won't be enough colostrum for the newborn baby. Some mothers and older children take a natural break around the time of birth and then start to tandem feed. Some children take a break because the colostrum in the milk doesn't taste so sweet. Some mothers carry on regardless, and there are no recorded side effects in newborn babies. Whatever your choice, be aware that you produce some colostrum for up to six weeks after birth, so your newborn will receive enough.

Nature's first food

I was ecstatic when my milk came in one hot August pitch-black night. Evie was about three days old. She was thirsty from the second she was born and was a very powerful sucker. She woke up and sucked my colostrum as normal. Then I felt masses of liquid on my tummy. I reached down to touch it with my fingers, and then I tasted it. It was warm, creamy and sweet. I had milk! I cried with joy. "What if you can't breastfeed?" was a common question that people had asked me. "I'm not even entering into that reality." I'd say. And I meant it. I had every reason to be able to breastfeed as I was healthy and had never experienced any breast issues. And so there it was, beautiful breastmilk for my beautiful baby. Evie gulped it down, first from one breast then from the one that had been leaking all over me.

I had so much milk and I got through loads of breastpads. I tried the washable organic ones but I couldn't keep up with supply and washing. As I planned to breastfeed until Evie wanted to stop, I bought a few hundred breastpads. Then about three months into breastfeeding I stopped leaking. It was a relief, but I wish someone had told me you don't leak forever! I still have the pads in my loft.

I wanted everyone to taste and experience my abundant milk supply. Evie's dad wouldn't taste it and I longed for a lover to give it to. What a gift. My whole life is focused around love, and milk given with love is a rarity for an adult to taste. How different it seemed to fear-filled stolen cow milk.

Speaking of lovers, raising children away from making love with your partner is an illogical concept. It's not real and leads to perversions of all kinds. Children who are breastfed are by default exposed to lovemaking when the mother has a partner. This creates extra love hormones for the child to enjoy. This is normal and natural so expect it to be reintroduced into our culture soon.

Nutritionally perfect

Breastmilk is usually nutritionally perfect. Women's bodies will sacrifice a lot to make and keep a healthy baby.

Lack of omega 3 (which converts to DHA) is common in our society now and can lead to many illnesses such as heart disease, hormone disruption and joint illness. An excess of omega 6 contributes to this imbalance, so when breastfeeding watch your intake of sunflower oil and other items high in omega 6.

As someone with a history of depression I went through a phase of taking 6 x 300mg vegan DHA a day because I was breastfeeding for years. Though our bodies convert omega 3 into DHA, it's not a very efficient process in most people. If you don't have enough DHA in your body, your gestating and breastfeeding child will suck it out of your brain. Hence "pregnancy brain" and "new mother memory". Your child needs lots of DHA during the first two years of his existence as his brain rapidly grows. Please ensure you have enough either through your diet or supplements. On top of at least 300mg of DHA, I'd recommend an abundance of hemp seeds, flax seeds and blue green algaes such as E3Live, Crystal Manna and Blue Manna.

Ooh, the pain

Evie was such a keen feeder but she had a really small mouth. I remember saying to her "Make a big mouth" and I'd feel that nipple pinch instead of the great big booboo swallow. As Veronika Robinson says: "It's not called nipple feeding, it's called breastfeeding". Much more of the breast should be in the mouth than most of us first realise. Only a few weeks into breastfeeding I got blisters on my nipples and all those who said "What if you can't breastfeed?" gathered round and asked "What now?" I was in such pain I couldn't say, but I wasn't going to give up. I went to a chemist and bought nipple guards. They are nipple and areola shaped silicone shields, with holes in the nipple for the milk to come through. Evie didn't mind that they were there and they offered immediate relief for me. I used them until the blisters cleared up and then there was no more pain. My nipples became tough and Evie enjoyed skin-to-skin loving from then on.

Most women give up on breastfeeding because the baby isn't attached correctly, which causes pain. If this happens to you, call your midwife and ask for extra lessons. My midwife came over and gave me a few extra feeding positions to try, which really helped. After about three months I could lie down and breastfeed, which revolutionised our lives yet again.

What's natural?

I always look to nature to see if I'm doing OK. I laugh at the funny image in my head of a lioness going "I don't know if I'll breastfeed when my rabble come along. I've got a hefty schedule of hunting and offal eating. That good-for-nothing husband doesn't help me one bit. Maybe if I bottle-feed, he could take over the night shift. I'm so tired. I wish Zebra were easier to catch. Life's too hard. I should check out the nurseries. I can't cope on my own". It's just not natural, is it?

Breastmilk is emotionally essential for bonding and it contains soothing hormones such as prolactin and oxytocin. These can't be replicated in formula milk.

Companies who make dummies in the UK are trying to adopt the American term pacifier. Whatever they're called, they're not nice and your child deserves better than that. They are far from natural and can cause an imbalance in the supply and demand of breastfeeding. There is absolutely no reason to give your child a fake nipple. If he needs love, give him love. If he needs to play, play with him. If he needs breastmilk, give him breastmilk. But never ever resort to that horrible fake plastic nipple which just screams at the child "This is your lot in life, sunshine. Love isn't real, get used to it now".

Cow milk is made for big animals with small brains.

Milk is species-specific

The life of the dairy cow and her calves is a tragic story from beginning to end. Can you imagine the emotional pain of a cow when she has her child stolen? What if someone came up to you and said "Miss Smith. You have two choices. We can kill you now or we can artificially inseminate you, let you gestate and birth a child, and then steal it from you when it's one day old. Then we'll strap you to a metal machine to remove your breastmilk every day for a year. We'll do this for about five years and then we'll kill you anyway". Though you're lucky enough not to have this as your destiny, conventional dairy cows don't have a choice. All intensively produced milk carries the energy of child loss, grief, sadness, pain, confusion and fear. Ask yourself if you want your family to resonate with that frequency.

A baby blue whale gains about 200 pounds (90 kilograms) a day. At seven months of age it starts to eat krill.

Cross-species dairy consumption is touted as an essential food for humans. The conventional milk and meat industries go hand in hand. Without one, the other would be prohibitively expensive. Cow milk is not essential for human health, and is often detrimental. For example, countries with the highest levels of dairy consumption also have the highest levels of osteoporosis. Yet so many people still drink animal milk because it's a cheap and abundant source of certain nutrients that are essential for growth.

When you remove the blinkers of cultural programming, the absurdity of conventional dairy farming and bottle-feeding becomes apparent. It isn't right, it isn't healthy and it only serves those profiting from it. Getting back in touch with our inner wisdom lets us create miracles for our families, our culture and ourselves. From now on, let's only choose the foods that are good and relevant for our families.

Full-term breastfeeding

One term that natural mothers are trying to abolish is "extended breastfeeding". This is a misleading term as it implies that breastfeeding beyond a certain age isn't natural. In fact, you can't breastfeed a child once he's lost his sucking reflex, so the Little Britain idea of "bitty" is actually impossible. Yet I do wonder what I'd do with David Walliams should I have the blessed opportunity to hold him close to my heart. Having said that, lovers can sometimes drink some milk during intimacy with a lactating woman. They can't get a whole meal out of it, though.

The World Health Organisation recommends that children are breastfed well into their second year and beyond as long as both mother and child are happy. The UK guidelines state that nothing but breastmilk should pass a child's lips for their first six months. Evie was seven months when she had her first food. She looked at me like it was from another planet. "What are you doing, mother? That's not your booboo!" According to information in *The Breastfeeding Answer Book* by Nancy Mohrbacher and Julie Stock, delaying the introduction of food from six months to seven months increases nutrient absorption by 60% for life.

Your child will thank you no end for full-term breastfeeding. I have a few friends who were breastfed beyond a year and they have much stronger immune systems than those who received less or no breastmilk.

The only way to ensure your child remains strong and immune for life is to allow him to develop a fully functioning immune system by full-term breastfeeding, choosing not to vaccinate, and feeding him real food as he grows. Breastmilk also contains hydrogen peroxide, anaesthetics and antibodies, which is why it's the great protector.

Once a child is denied basic rights such as full-term breastfeeding on cue, skin-to-skin contact, co-sleeping, being carried and having full mummy access at all times, his brain rewires to cope with the trauma. According to Professor Margot Sunderland in her book *The Science Of Parenting*, children who are left to cry to sleep are more likely to become addicts in later life. Children who aren't fully breastfed end up with separation issues.

The anthropological age for a human child to wean off breastmilk is around four to seven years. This is evident in our development when compared to other animals. "Milk" teeth also drop out around that time. This time also coincides with the child finding independent activities in other ways, such as extended time with the father or other children. As mothers, we need to ensure we're always around if our children need us, but we're not holding onto them due to our unfulfilled needs.

A young adult is still your child, so think about how healthy you want her to be in later life.

You never need to know if your child is getting enough milk. Your close and loving relationship with her goes way beyond what your left-brain can tell you. You're an instinctive being, just like all those other breastfeeding wild animals that don't know how many millilitres their child is taking in. If your child isn't showing signs of dehydration (indented fontanel and dry nappies) then she is receiving enough breastmilk. When full-term breastfeeding, your child doesn't need other milk. However, as she starts eating food she may become interested in other drinks. Evie loved coconut water, diluted fruit juice, green juices, smoothies and water from seven months of age.

If you talk to children who have been breastfed full term, they'll tell you that the best food ever is breastmilk. They know and can articulate that. After Evie finished breastfeeding, I asked how she remembered the taste. "It tasted of avocados and September." Maybe she felt the autumn of her infancy.

Poooooh!

Evie's poo always smelled so sweet and clean in her first seven months. When I once had to change her nappy while at a friend's house, my friend fetched me a nappy bag. I asked her why I needed it, and she said for the smell. I was confused. "What smell?" I shoved the nappy under her nose. Now she was confused. Her baby was only a bit younger than Evie, but was on formula. To put it politely, she didn't produce poos that smelled as fragrant as Evie's.

Not sleeping through the night

Breastfed children do not sleep through the night. A healthy breastfeeding child will wake several times to feed and snuggle, yet you may not even notice if you're sleeping next to her. Evie stopped breastfeeding on her fourth birthday and started sleeping through the night about a week later.

Your child has a stomach the size of its fist, which empties quickly because breastmilk is very easy to digest. This is why your child will wake up several times throughout the night. By contrast, formula milk is hard to digest, having all sorts of unnatural components to it. This is why bottle-fed children sleep so well: their bodies are attempting to assimilate this artificial "food".

Enlist the support of friends and family to love your baby first thing in the morning at least once a week so you can catch up on your sleep. If you can't do this, ensure you lie down whenever you're breastfeeding and snuggle up close to your child. This is a perfect time to nod off. Make sure you don't have "too much to do". The everyday things such as cleaning can wait until you are feeling less tired. A clean house isn't as important as a sane mother.

Wet nursing and breastfeeding alternatives

My best friend Kate Magic once breastfed Evie so that I could go on a date with Admmm. Evie was about fourteen months old at the time and still very much attached to me. Kate is a raw foodist, so she fed Evie with the same quality milk as she was used to. Admmm and I had the most wonderful evening, and I collected Evie at 1am. She snuggled us all night long. Those few hours off were really precious and most deserved. Most tribal women breastfeed each other's children, and I am happy to have the same mindset as them.

If you've turned your nose up at the thought of breastfeeding another child, ask yourself why. Evie was still being loved by one of my tribe and she received the nourishment she required. It was also a great experience for Kate as her own three children were all boys. She said Evie was very gentle and it was really different for her. I had a lovely time with Admmm, which I really needed. All four of us were ecstatic about the experience.

Wet nurses were very common a few years ago in the UK. Even now, mothers who genuinely can't breastfeed can often find sympathetic and abundant mothers who will express milk for the milkless mother to feed her child. If you can't breastfeed your child or find a wet nurse, please do not attempt to create your own formula for the first six months, as your baby could end up permanently damaged. There is a place for animal milk in situations like this. Look at *Nanny Care Goat Milk Nutrition*, which isn't organically certified but comes from grass-fed New Zealand goats. After six months, you could introduce raw and organic goat milk or yoghurt.

Where breast augmentation is now seen as the norm, wet nursing is becoming popular again. There are agencies in the USA dedicated to this service for mothers who can't breastfeed due to these operations and other reasons.

Achieving the impossible — milk men

Breastfeeding is so wonderful and important that some adoptive mothers and even fathers have managed it. Both genders can learn how to lactate using a special technique. A breast is a breast: men don't just have nipples; they actually have mammary glands. The natural mothering author Laura Shanley and others believe that men have these glands not as a weird leftover from before their gender was determined in the womb, but as an emergency supply for breastmilk should it be needed. Such is the essential nature of breastmilk. Shanley's husband produced breastmilk, and she recounts his story in her classic book *Unassisted Childbirth*.

Let it all flow

Please don't consider being part of the mainstream when it comes to breastfeeding your child. You don't have to create an artificial world for your baby. Let her stay in touch with herself and with you. Keep her connected. Don't sell your child short at such a young age in life. Only breastfeeding, co-sleeping and babywearing can keep a baby as happy as she deserves to be.

We are the revolutionaries of our generation. We birth and raise children, run houses and work full time. Doing all that while remaining a divine goddess is intense yet not impossible, because we have a secret weapon: support.

When we live communally, allowing grandparents, older siblings, friends and other relatives to help, full term breastfeeding and natural parenting become easy and fun. We all love helping people, and we can also learn to love to be helped. Mothering with help is an absolute joy, and everyone wins.

After breastmilk

Once a child has weaned she can still enjoy milky drinks in the form of nut and seed milks. Seed milks made with pumpkin, Salba or hemp contain lots of omega 3. You can increase the bioavailability of this by adding a touch of coconut oil as well as hemp oil, Udo's Choice oil or flax oil.

Being close to your heartbeat is still very comforting for your child, so snuggle her often. Children are never too old to benefit from a lovely warm mummy-cuddle, but you might have to wear a bra!

Further information

The Drinks Are On Me — Veronika Sophia Robinson

The Womanly Art Of Breastfeeding — La Leche League

Michele: The Nursing Toddler — Jane Pinczuic

When Breastfeeding Is Not An Option — Peggy Robin

Fabulous Fats (DVD) — Mary Toscano

Milk Men: youtube.com/watch?v=DiXp_See_Bs — an inspiring short film on male lactation.

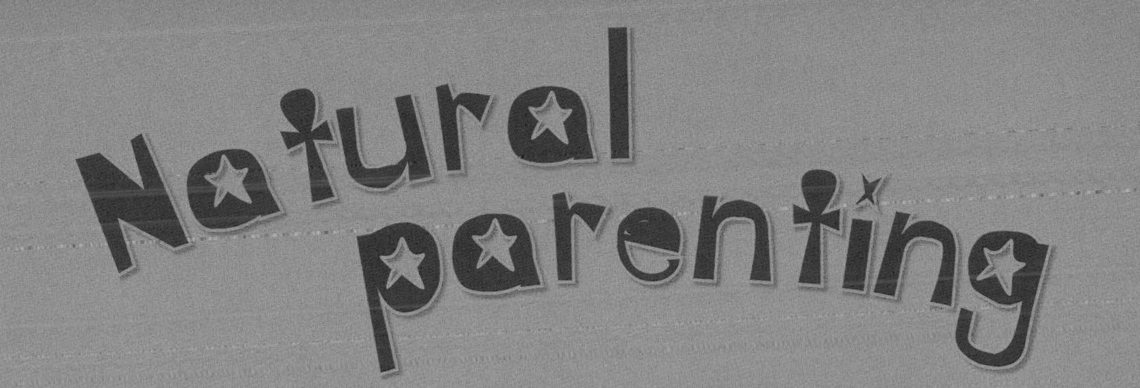
Natural parenting

Ecstatic birthing

Much of this ecstatic birthing information was inspired by Binnie A Dansby. I fully recommend you support her work.

> *Conceive the birth of consciousness that is certain that it is safe in the world, supported and loved. Conceive the birth of consciousness that embraces feelings and opens easily to higher and higher levels of energy. Conceive the birth of consciousness that knows that it has a choice about what to think about every experience. Conceive the birth of consciousness that perceives itself as innocent, an expression of love co-creating. Conceive the birth of consciousness that remembers its Soul's Purpose, to serve by being present without judgment. Conceive the possibility of all the members of the Family of Humanity participating fully in the creative process, Birth and Life, with a sense of accomplishment and satisfaction.*
>
> — Binnie A Dansby, 2000

Binnie's work in promoting ecstatic birthing helps greatly in removing the fear of birth that has been handed down from generation to generation. Most young girls and women dread the idea of giving birth. They think that childbirth will be the most traumatic, painful and disturbing thing that could happen to them.

The ecstatic birth movement works hard to change all that. It was kick-started by Binnie Dansby in 1987 at a talk and is thriving to this day. Pre-natal mothers trained in and prepared for an ecstatic birth have had some of the least traumatic births ever witnessed, some almost pain-free, and only three per cent requiring any medical intervention. Compare that to the national average of eighty per cent of standard births needing medical intervention. This can only lead me to reaffirm one thing: what you expect is what you get. If you are programmed to anticipate pain, humiliation and medical intervention, you will get it.

Ecstatic birthing allows nature's most gorgeous experience to be just that. It is about surrendering and empowering, accepting our place in this magical cycle of life and death. Embracing it. Saying yes to it. Allowing it. Allowing our bodies to change, shift and ultimately give new life to our awe-inspiring planet.

Why would you want anything other than an ecstatic birth?

When we make a decision in a heightened state, it tends to have a deep and lasting effect. Making the conscious choice to have an ecstatic birth is the first step towards creating that result. Once you've made that commitment to experiencing an ecstatic birth, it's more likely that the universe will conspire to give you just what you need to make it happen.

Preparing for your birth

An ecstatic birth requires preparation on physiological, emotional and physical levels. Nothing should be left to chance. We now have an abundance of resources and tools for inner and outer preparation. Go for the ones that feel best for you. Support yourself and intentionally nurture your environment to have a greater chance of being nurtured in return.

Accepting the support of others is of equal, if not even more, importance. Binnie has observed that this is the most difficult task for many women. I ended up having a c-section though my initial birthing plans included a hands-off home birth in a pool. I went on a hypnobirthing course and I took part in Active Birth classes as well as weekly pregnancy yoga. Before Evie's birth I didn't have the midwife support that I needed. They refused to attend her birthing at home as she was a bum-first breech. It was only a couple of years later when I met a natural midwife, told her my story and asked her what she'd have done. "I'd have helped you give birth." Support is everything, so do look for it, ask for it and expect it.

Creativity activates different areas of your brain, which will ultimately put you in a stronger emotional space when giving birth. Explore and express your creative potential with art, poetry and new languages. These are also great skills to use with your new child.

Get involved with communities who are aware of ecstatic birthing. Surround yourself with books, images and videos of these births. There are many ecstatic birthing films on YouTube. Spend your time focusing on what inspires and uplifts you. Live the life of an ecstatic being.

Vaccinations

"The greatest lie ever told is that vaccines are safe and effective."
— **Dr Len Horowitz**

"Tell a lie loud enough and long enough and people will believe it."
— **Adolf Hitler**

Parents are pressurised into vaccinating their children by government campaigns and GPs. However, there is constant uncertainty as to whether these vaccinations are effective and safe.

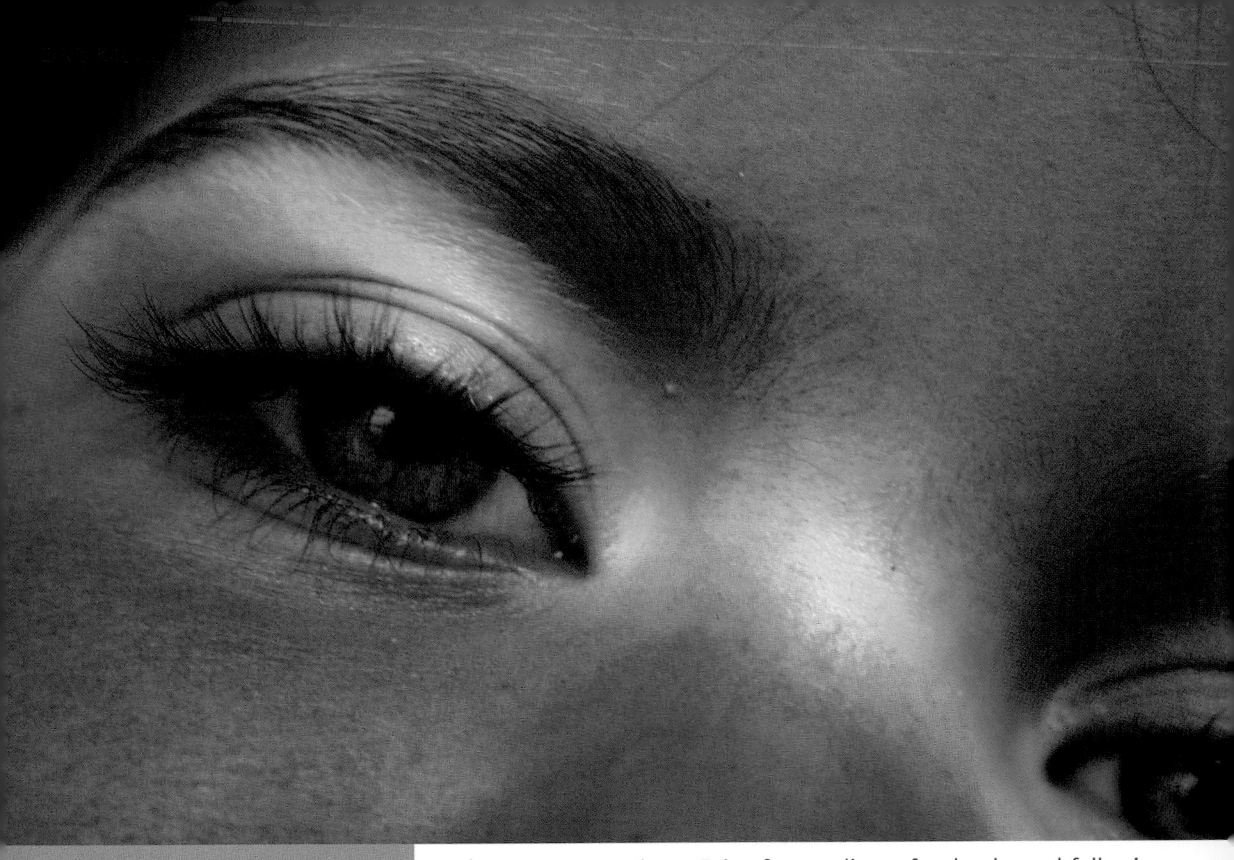

I chose not to vaccinate Evie after reading a few books and following my heart. If I wasn't going to give her food that would compromise her immune system, why would I do it with "medicine"? As a mother, I want to love, nourish and protect her. I want to raise her without the left-brained patriarchal pressure that is prevalent in our society. Vaccinations are about as left-brained as you can get.

Full-term breastfeeding offers much more immunisation than short-term or no breastfeeding. Childhood illnesses are much milder or non-existent with breastfed children. Childhood illnesses exist to strengthen the body and to build defences against more serious diseases later in life. The drastic and devastating effects of childhood illnesses usually affect children who don't have such a great nutritional start in life.

In America, the US Government's Vaccine Adverse Event Reporting System (part of the FDA) monitors vaccinations and problems arising from them. Unfortunately only about 1-10% of adverse events ever get reported to the FDA.

- Officially in 1998, 88 infant deaths occurred due to a vaccination.
- Officially in 2000, 73 infant deaths occurred due to a vaccination.

You may assume that these deaths are nothing in comparison to potential lives saved, so consider the words of integrative medicine pioneer Dr Philip Incao: "Incredible as it sounds, such a common sense, controlled study comparing vaccinated to unvaccinated children has never been done in America for any vaccination. In other words we have no information that shows that vaccines work as they are intended to work."

At the annual meeting of the American Association of Physicians and Surgeons in October 2000 a resolution was passed saying that "Safety testing of many vaccines is limited and the data are unavailable for independent scrutiny, so that mass vaccination is equivalent to human experimentation." Visit www.aapsonline.org for the full report.

On 29th January 2001, Jock Doubleday (director of the non-profit corporation Natural Woman, Natural Man Inc) offered $20,000 to the first medical doctor or pharmaceutical company CEO who would publicly drink a mixture of standard vaccine additives (containing no virus), scaled up to the participant's body weight. The offer had no valid takers. On 1st August 2006, the offer was bumped to $75,000 and has increased at a rate of $5,000 per month. To date, Jock tells me that the offer has had no valid takers, and now stands in excess of $100,000.

If you look hard enough, there is "evidence" both ways about the effectiveness and risks of vaccination. This is why I urge you to read the books and other resources listed below. Only you can make your own mind up.

Evie's first aid kit

Our first aid kit is simple and very effective. I hope this list encourages you to build your own — adding your favourite other remedies as you go. In addition to these products, I have a stash of plasters for cuts, grazes and rainy days.

I often mix some of these ingredients up and use them together, depending on the situation. I just use my intuition and always get it right. All these products work great with each other. For example, when my friend had an unidentified allergic attack her face, neck and shoulders became red and swollen. I mixed up a small amount of DMSO (to help the other ingredients penetrate the skin quickly) with MSM powder, silver and 3% hydrogen peroxide. I brushed this onto her as she drank about three dessertspoons of MSM powder dissolved in water. The reaction stopped immediately and reversed within minutes. After about twenty minutes she washed the mixture off. Interestingly I'd missed a tiny area of skin on her shoulder that was still red and sore. If you want to use these natural products for yourself and your family, have a look at protocols on the Internet and check out the Further information listed below.

I find that with these tools lying around, I have no need for other herbs or cures when we hurt ourselves. Our natural diet (which contains herbs and medicinal mushrooms) ensures we're very healthy most of the time, and these little emergencies do wonders when we need them. However, I do exercise caution and refer to books on children if I think Evie needs further help or the advice of a doctor.

MSM aloe lotion

I buy this proprietary brand from Sunfood Nutrition in the USA. It contains silver, aloe vera and MSM, with a whole host of other herbs. I find it invaluable whenever faced with stings, bites, burns, inflammation and discomfort. Don't use it on your private parts if you're sensitive as it's very strong! If you have post-baby piles, thrush or even cellulite, try this. As long as the skin's unbroken, this is the best topical remedy I've ever used.

Be careful as it's very potent. For your child, use neat if it's just a dot, or dilute with body cream 1:1 if you're spreading it over his skin. Try a patch test on healthy skin in advance to make sure you have the correct ratio in an emergency.

Vitamin C (in the form of ester for bioavailability)

As one of the best immune boosters known, you can add this powder into food or sweet drinks once your child is six months old. Start with 600mg a day, and add 100mg a day every month. For example, once your child is one year old, use 1200mg a day. This may seem a lot but vitamin C has no toxic level and it's the best guard against most illnesses that I know of. We need our children to be exposed to childhood diseases such as measles. This causes the immune system to mature and respond correctly to adult diseases. Supplementing with vitamin C enables our children to remain "healthy" and not suffer while in the incubation and recovery periods. This process is known as natural or cellular immunity, not just antibody protection.

Vitamin C is also a natural antibiotic if taken in sufficient doses. It's hard to get a toddler to take a teaspoon of pure vitamin C, but if her health depends on it, there are ways. "A spoon full of agave nectar helps the medicine go down..." Dr Andrew Saul, a vitamin C expert, recommends 35 grams a day for antibiotic use in an adult, divided into 24 hourly doses. This would need to be reduced significantly for a baby or toddler. Though you can't overdose on Vitamin C, at this level a temporary upset of the tummy may be experienced.

If you can't get vitamin C ester, then look for magnesium ascorbate. Ascorbic acid can be used in an emergency.

Ionic (angstrom) silver

Ionic minerals are smaller than colloidal minerals, and are fully absorbable by the body when taken sublingually (under the tongue). Silver kills all pathogens such as viruses, bacteria and moulds that it meets within about six minutes. If Evie displays any signs of illness at all, I give her a dessertspoon of silver each day until the symptoms disappear. In fact I could give her this silver every day as ionic silver does not build up in the body and is non-toxic. Topically I put silver on cuts, infections and spots.

If Evie gets conjunctivitis (she's only had it twice) I use an eye-drop formula called Rich's MSM Water Drops, which contains ionic silver. When breastfeeding, I used my milk to rinse Evie's eyes.

I love the fact that there are now plasters, tea towels and stockings impregnated with silver available to buy and in hospitals. I've been a fan of silver for years, so I'm really glad it's coming back into mainstream therapeutic fashion again.

Ozonated olive oil

Great for infections, ozonated olive oil can even be eaten (I haven't tried this on myself or Evie, though I've used it as a rectal implant). Ozone kills pathogens on contact, and I use it daily as a moisturiser. I've used it successfully with Evie on a mild but persistent rash (with a drop of DMSO). Again, it's wise to dilute or patch test this on young skin as it can be very strong.

If Evie ever had a deep or persistent infection of any sort I'd get her some ozone insufflation or, in an emergency, use ozone oil with DMSO. In a potentially more serious case, I'd find a practitioner who offered ozone autohaemotherapy.

MSM powder or crystals

I've used this on three friends who were suffering from major allergic reactions (two were as a result of eating nuts, one wasn't identified). Each time, the person was ready to go to hospital or use an adrenaline shot. Each time, the symptoms subsided within minutes of taking MSM powder.

If Evie suffered from any allergy, I'd ensure she carried a bag of MSM around with her at all times. MSM is one of the most potent and fast-acting natural medicines I've ever encountered.

People have conquered all allergy symptoms by taking one dessertspoon of MSM a day for three months. If you want to try this with your child, reduce the dosage according to her weight and give it to her in something really sweet to disguise the very bitter flavour. Enlist the help of a kinesiologist, who can check for allergies before and after the treatment.

DMSO

DMSO was first synthesised by a Russian chemist called Alexander Saytzeff in 1867. A century later it was being used in medicine as a team at the University of Oregon Medical School had discovered it could penetrate the skin (as a drug delivery system) without damaging it.

It is great when used with other products but is not one to experiment wildly with. If you're interested in using DMSO please read up on it first. Always keep it away from children and away from eyes. I've never found DMSO in the UK, but it's easy to buy in liquid or gel form on the Internet from the USA.

Bach Flower Rescue Remedy

This is great for shock and trauma. It comes in a small bottle so is easy to carry round. Anyone of any age can take it, and it works very quickly.

Arnica, homoeopathic

The Helios brand is vegan (not lactose-based like most homeopathic tablets). It's very effective for falls, bruising and trauma.

Hydrogen peroxide, food grade

I have 35% hydrogen peroxide in my fridge, stored safely away from Evie because it's corrosive to skin at that level of concentration. I use this to sterilise kitchen equipment and my own medicine concoctions. I also bathe in it, with lots of added water.

I also have 3% hydrogen peroxide in a spray bottle, which is safe enough to administer in any amount to Evie. Topically, it's great for cuts, infections and rashes. Orally, it's wonderful to use when brushing teeth or just after. At 3% it's safe to swallow, so there's no cause for concern, unlike with conventional toothpaste. It's also great to spray all over the skin after a bath as it keeps pathogens at bay and restores pH balance. Keep hydrogen peroxide away from eyes.

Olive leaf and pau d'arco tea

I make this brew for Evie and me every day. It keeps our immune systems strong and less susceptible to viruses, bacteria, parasites and mould. It can be used topically and in the bath too. We sometimes use leftover tea in our smoothies.

Co-sleeping

What could be more comfortable, natural, reassuring and deliciously fragrant than lying naked in bed with your warm, sleepy, suckling baby? This is the most rewarding part of parenting. During recent years, more people have woken up to the fact that co-sleeping is beneficial for all involved.

Sudden Infant Death Syndrome (SIDS) rarely happens with co-sleeping children unless the parent has been drinking alcohol or taking drugs. If you're sober and in a bed (not on a sofa), you can't roll onto your sleeping child and kill it. NHS guidelines reaffirm this by saying

that co-sleeping is not a problem in itself; only if it's combined with cigarettes, drugs or alcohol. A mother's breath on her baby in sleep stimulates the baby's heart and breathing function, and her external body heat adjusts to keep the baby's temperature perfect, protecting against SIDS. In countries like China and Japan, where co-sleeping is a normal part of life, SIDS is virtually unheard of.

I slept with Evie from day one. I put my bed on the floor so she couldn't hurt herself if she fell out. She had her own bedroom after about one year, and she started sleeping in her own bed after about two and a half years. At that age she'd wake up, breastfeed back to sleep, and then wake up again a few hours later to repeat the cycle. When I went to bed she'd come in with me and we'd sleep in each other's arms. Until she stopped breastfeeding she still got in bed with me in the small hours and snuggled right up to me. These days, I still often wake up with a four year old in bed with me, and I can't remember how she got there.

If you make your child sleep in another bed or room then expect to be more exhausted than you need to be, because you'll have to get up several times a night. Children will naturally gravitate to their own bed in time, so forcing it upon them is not only distressing, it's unnecessary.

Babywearing

Babywearing is the practice of wearing or carrying a small child in a sling, piece of cloth or other carrier. People from around the world have worn their babies for millennia. Babywearing is a form of transport, which adds to the bonding experience.

There are many benefits to baby wearing:

- The mother's progesterone levels are increased through physical contact with the infant, leading to a more intimate maternal bond, easier breastfeeding and better care.
- Infants who are carried are calmer because all of their primal/ survival needs are met. The caregiver can be seen, heard, smelled, touched and tasted, and can provide feeding.
- Consistent motion is necessary for continuing neural development, gastrointestinal and respiratory health and to establish balance (inner ear development) and muscle tone.
- Parental rhythms such as walking and heartbeat have a balancing and soothing effect.
- Infants are "humanised" earlier by developing socially. Babies who are closer to adults can study facial expressions, learn languages faster and become familiar with body language.

- Independence is established earlier (according to Desmond Morris in his book *Babywatching*).
- You have two free hands to mothertask: do the laundry, juice the cucumbers and keep your baby content.
- Some slings are designed for easy breastfeeding, without moving or disturbing the baby.
- Slings take up less space than pushchairs.

Infant feeding and babywearing

Premature and underweight babies gain weight faster when they are worn. Held close to the mother, the baby can breastfeed more often and for longer intervals. Kangaroo care (keeping a small baby on the parent's chest) has shown clear benefits to premature and ill infants. In her book *Kangarooing Our Little Miracles*, Krisanne Larimer mentions a pioneering kangaroo care initiative in Columbia where it "was found to be an inexpensive and very beneficial experience to babies... The mortality rate fell from 70% to 30%."

Spend time mastering the art of breastfeeding without a carrier, and then enjoy it with a sling. Where breastfeeding difficulties exist, you can babywear and have free hands to deal with breast pumps, bottles and other supplementation devices.

Babywearing safety considerations

If you're wearing your baby, as opposed to just carrying her, be more aware of uneven pavements as you can't see downwards very well.

In a sling rather than a pushchair or vibrating rocking chair your baby will find all those shiny and exciting things much easier to grasp, so ensure all hot drinks and dangerous objects are out of reach.

Ensure your baby is in the right position so her hips, pelvis and spine grow correctly. I found a tight wrap-around sling to be better for Evie from birth to three months, and the over-one-shoulder type better as she grew. Follow knotting and tying instructions carefully, and if you're unsure, ask for help at a sling-selling shop or from your health visitor.

Conscious communication

Most of our thinking, acting and speaking is unconscious. We can find ourselves running into conflict, miscommunications, inauthentic interchanges and general obstacles on a daily basis because of our inability to truly consciously communicate with one another and ourselves. Few people are taught the fundamentals of real communication in schools or at home. Children will mimic our methods of communication. Learning the basics of conscious communication before you conceive is a great idea, but it's never too late.

According to Susan Campbell in her book *Saying What's Real*, "Almost 90% of all human communication comes from the (usually unconscious) intent to control." We have no need to control our children; we want to lovingly guide them on their way to becoming an adult.

Around 80% of all the input our children receive is negative ("don't do that", "no, not like that"). A child is like a sponge; she receives and believes anything that you say to her. Negative reinforcement causes children to grow into adults who think they're not good enough, can't do anything right and don't deserve the things that make them feel good.

When parents say "No" too often, the meaning of the word gets diluted. When you really mean no, it may not be effective. "Let's do this instead" is a great alternative to the N word. By adding simple positive statements your child will feel less suppressed and much more nourished. A hug and an "I love you" works wonders in all circumstances.

If your child has misbehaved, talk gently and calmly about why she could make a different choice next time. With Evie, I say "I don't do

that, do I?" Because she adores me, I can see her head ticking "No, mummy doesn't do that". Even with ingrained behavioural patterns, love, not punishment, changes children successfully.

When you know how to communicate more consciously, enabling true connection, the relationship with your child and other family members becomes less stressful and much more joyful.

Free-range children

"Remember, any attempt to force or structure learning in the under fives, actually backfires. It's like ripping open a rosebud to get it to bloom." — **Steve Biddulph**

Every child is unique. Our average school system shoehorns kids into standard boxes. This suppresses their natural development and ultimately causes them to become useful and obedient members of society. Weakened, they blindly contribute to our economy, become cannon fodder or perhaps even become teachers themselves to keep society's cog wheels turning. Some children go through the normal school system and find another way to live their lives. Yet for the majority, their motivation, inspiration and confidence is sucked out of them. Most children are right-brained when entering school, yet only two per cent of school leavers remain highly creative. Though it's possible to re-establish this creativity with practice, it's easier never to lose it in the school system in the first place.

I hope that a new breed of parents will make decisions that serve their children to the fullest, allowing them to blossom and embrace their glorious destiny. This could happen in many ways. There are schools that use carefully tuned techniques to cater for each child in an individual way, fertilising their strengths and giving support where needed in areas that are not as developed. The Steiner movement has led the field in this area.

Children can be educated without going to school. For example, a group of like-minded parents and guardians could find a space to set up their own educational venue. In this venue, children could develop a full spectrum of skills, including movement and co-ordination, conscious communication, relating skills, yoga, reiki, gardening, survival and wildlife experiences. More traditional subjects such as reading, writing and mathematics could feature, but not at the expense of other life skills.

There is an "unschooling" movement in the UK and beyond that allows children complete freedom to do what they want, when they want. The theory is that the children will develop everything at their own pace and in their own way. It produces intelligent, independent and skilled young adults. When homeschooling or unschooling we need to ensure our children have adequate amounts of play times with other children.

My school memories are not happy ones. Being told to stand for a man entering the room, who was then going to bore me with biased viewpoints about the world wars, wasn't as exciting as staring out of the window. Being unable to fully express my creative side because of endless irrelevant lessons only led to frustration, rebellion and a feeling of extreme disconnection.

Some children thrive in school environments and that's great. As for Evie, may she have a free-range childhood; actually, may she have a free-range life!

Further information

Flood Your Body With Oxygen — Ed McCabe. Shocking information on the healing power of oxygen, hydrogen peroxide and ozone.

DMSO Nature's Healer — Morton Walker. Essential reading if you're interested in using DMSO.

Raising A Vaccine Free Child — Wendy Lydall.

The Vaccination Dilemma — Sophia Christine Murphy.

The Continuum Concept — Jean Leidloff. Jean's observations in tribal society can teach us a lot. It's not natural to be with children of just one age, and it's not natural to spend countless hours learning abstract ideas with a stranger. The tribe she studied were happier than any western family I've ever met.

The Science of Parenting — Dr Margot Sunderland. This book is based on over 700 scientific studies on child development. Use her tools and watch your child flourish into a well-adjusted and happy adult.

Ecstatic Birth — ecstaticbirth.com. Binnie A Dansby's revolutionary resourceful web site.

Doctor Yourself — doctoryourself.com. Dr Andrew Saul's book and huge online resource on vitamin C therapies and more.

Vaccine Risk Awareness — vaccineriskawareness.com. Joanna Karpasea Jone's book (Vaccination) and online resource for up to date vaccination information.

All about Evie

I never wanted children. I had three lovely nephews, a great social life, and I was scared stiff of anything that pooed and sicked and gave women stretch marks.

People used to say to me that I'd change once I was in my thirties, and I'd shake my head. It really wasn't an issue to me. I was a typical out-of-touch career girl who'd been hormonally screwed up for years because of the pill, late nights and undesirable food.

Then my thirties came. I'd changed my food, long since ditched the pill, and I started to get these twinges. I'd say "Oh, I'll have a baby when I'm 35", because 35 seemed so far in the future that it was intangible.

In my life, I'd flitted from man to man, from city to city, from country to country, from job to job, from house to house. Then I decided to do a bit of online dating. I worked from home, so meeting a man was tough as I often went for days without seeing a soul (this suited my reclusive tendencies and persistent agoraphobia). I met a man online called Matt. We chatted and we met for real. As I was talking to him I saw this beautiful shining glowing entity in the corner of the room. It was golden and rotating, like a celestial disco ball. I said to Matt, "Can you see that?" but it was gone. I thought no more of it.

A few weeks later, I went to the USA for a holiday and to give a lecture. I visited the fascinating Tree of Life in Arizona, a living foods healing retreat. I walked their labyrinth and spent time in the goddess garden. I felt like a full power woman for the first time in my life.

I came back to the UK and made Matt and myself some maca and raw cacao smoothies. The potency of the drinks and our enjoyment of each other helped a little spirit come to earth. The day after, I started a seven day fast on just water. Then I felt a bit strange "down there" so went to the doctors thinking I had cancer!

The doctor pretty much told me I was being silly, but I insisted: "There's something going on. It feels different!" Well, it transpired that there *was* a growth, but it was a good one! Discovering I was pregnant was both shocking and wonderful. I hardly knew Matt, yet he was to become the father of my child. As soon as we did the pregnancy test, my psychic sister phoned me. After the hysterics had died down, she told me that she'd dreamed the night before that she was pregnant and couldn't understand why, as she'd had her tubes tied.

Matt and I talked about our options. There were two. One was that we had the baby. The other was that *I* had the baby. I was more than happy to never see him again and have the baby as a single mother.

Matt said he wanted to do "what's right." This actually meant he wanted to do what people are conditioned to think is right.

Something in the oven

My parents had been on a tour of the USA and Mexico for my Dad's 60th birthday. I went to their house to welcome them home. I texted them as they were driving from the airport: "Don't eat anything, I've got something in the oven." My mum was so tired, she didn't pick up on my hint.

Then at nine weeks, I started to bleed. I knew miscarriage before twelve weeks was common, but despite the widespread belief that you should keep your mouth shut until you're three months gone I'd already told everyone. I'm a loudmouth and can't keep secrets about myself, and I was excited and very healthy, so I never thought I'd have a problem pregnancy. Also, you can lose a baby after three months, when people know anyway. Either way, if you lose a baby you're still emotionally sore, whether it's before or after twelve weeks. I couldn't imagine having to deal with the emotional pain alone and in secret. I guess that's part of the society we live in – sweep it under the carpet and keep a stiff upper lip.

When suddenly faced with the threat of losing this precious person I cried and cried and was unexpectedly alone. I was alone because Matt and I didn't live together and he was finding the pregnancy really hard to deal with. When the doctors told me there was nothing they could do, and I should just go home and take it easy, I did just that: alone and with a baby that maybe wasn't going to make it. The bleeding continued and I started eating. I ate to fill the hole of a "boyfriend" who wasn't supportive or even present, and I ate to fill the hole of maybe losing my child. I made a big old mess in my kitchen and I left it there for Matt to clear up. When he came over to visit a week later, I asked him to clean my kitchen. He went on and on about how he'd come to see me, not clear up after me. I explained that I was told to take it easy (there was a really big mess), but he insisted that it wasn't up to him. That was the beginning of the end for Matt and me, though it actually dragged out until Evie was about seven months old. There I was in a massive hormonal turmoil, and the man who helped create it wouldn't even help me clean my kitchen.

Though I wasn't planning on having any scans at all, we had one to see if the baby was still alive. And there she was, alive and well. I was so relieved.

Eventually the unexplained bleeding stopped, but the eating didn't. I'd got into cooked food for the first time in four years. Cooked food is great for covering up your emotions, for filling those holes left by your unmet expectations and hopes.

At five months, my hips gave way. I'm hyperflexible and the weight I'd put on, coupled with the hormone relaxin flooding my body, caused me to be more floppy than normal. It hurt to walk and I had to do so at a snail's pace. I was an eight stone astanga yogini raw foodist before this. Suddenly I was fat, unable to walk and stuck to the telly with soya ice cream in my hand. You get this insatiable appetite for icy food when you're pregnant, and as soon as you have the baby it goes, in an instant.

A natural birth?

We had another scan at twenty weeks. I didn't want one and Matt did, so I figured that if I gave in to this, then when it came to the really important issues such as vaccinations I'd be able to say, "Look, I'm flexible on some things, but not this." Evie was pronounced normal.

For later tests the midwife felt my baby's position with her hands. At some point she proclaimed "The baby's breech," then a few weeks later, "The baby's still breech," then a while later, "Er, this baby still hasn't turned." At some point I became concerned. I'd already gone from wanting to give birth unassisted under a tree to booking a pool and homebirth. I wanted a natural birth so much, I'd attended a hypnobirthing course, active birth classes and pregnancy yoga, and I'd read every book I could find on natural birthing. I was so excited about the prospect of birthing my baby, and constantly imagined the day that I'd give birth ecstatically and naturally.

But this baby had other ideas. After yet another scan (because of her position), it was apparent that she was a bum-first breech, folded over with straight legs and in exactly the same position as I was, 35 years before. I tried everything in the holistic world to turn her. Finally we attempted an ECV (external cephalic version). I tried it without the muscle relaxing jab first, and then when that failed I tried it with the jab. That also failed. For a long time I wondered why on earth my child wouldn't want a stress-free home birth under water. And of course I couldn't come to any conclusion because I didn't know, and I didn't know what to do.

We listed all the options, and nobody pressured me into making a decision. I thought of nothing else for days, and I cried so much. The midwives were wholly unsupportive of me attempting a home birth. In fact, they said they wouldn't attend, but would accept me going to hospital for an "extraction". Finally, for many reasons, and probably because I was guided to, I decided to have an elective c-section. I was more surprised than anyone by my decision.

I still wrote a birth plan, which the hospital honoured in its entirety apart from the request to prolong the cord cutting. After I convinced the staff to delay the birthing date, we were booked in just two days from the baby's "due date". I wanted to give her as much chance as possible to turn, but in reality I knew she was stuck fast by now. I'd talk to her about all this, saying that if I went into labour before the c-section was due, then it meant she wanted me to birth her naturally. I even fantasised about going into labour alone and birthing alone.

However, the reality was that I knew of no first-time mother who'd given birth to a breech in this position, and I knew of the permanent damage that my mum suffered after birthing me. In addition, there were several other breeches in the hospital when I was born, and they all suffered brain damage. I didn't care about the medical statistics that are given to scare women with breech babies because statistics can make anything look true; I cared about the experiences of the only people I know to have birthed breech babies.

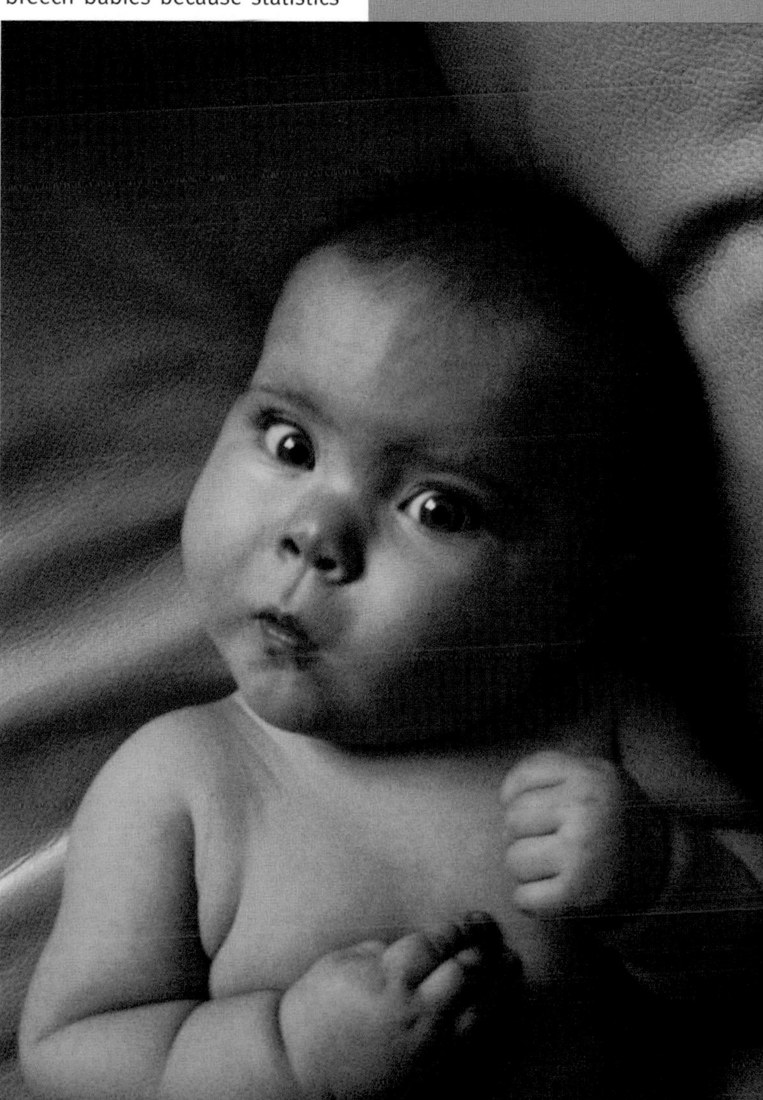

As I continued to attempt all the baby-turning tricks I also started taking Bach Flower Rescue Remedy. Though I'd accepted I wasn't likely to have the birth I so wished for, I was still incredibly distressed by it. I survived the emotional pain of this by knowing that I'd still have a lovely baby afterwards.

The birthing

On the 5th of August 2004 (Red Solar Moon) we arrived at the hospital; my baby was due to be born at around 3.30pm. Earlier, I'd taken a homeopathic remedy for panic and anxiety from my birthing kit from Helios. That kit came in so handy, even though we didn't have a natural birth. I took arnica pills for several days after the birth, and a couple just before.

It was so surreal in the theatre. I started to get scared but something big was guiding me all the way. Matt was rushed into another room and I was sitting on a bed surrounded by people dressed in green. I discussed my birth plan with my surgeon. She finally consented to me being naked, which was against her protocol.

When Matt came back in dressed in green, all the tubes and needles started finding their way into me. The medical team were so friendly and talked me through everything. One of the doctors said he'd given me some heroin, but it was cleaner than you'd get off the streets. I'm sure it went to my brain because I lost all my senses; I was total putty. He assured me it wouldn't have gone to my brain, so who knows what hormones were flooding me.

The physical feeling was odd. I wasn't numb but my legs felt like they were made of that tin foil that marathon runners wrap themselves up in after a race. Then I was catheterised, which I couldn't feel at all. I talked total gibberish throughout all these gentle pokings and proddings. At no time did any of the theatre team talk down to me, or talk about anything other than the birthing.

We were ready. Lying there naked and without a screen in place, my tummy was cut open by the two female surgeons. Our birthing music played (which my baby had heard every day for months beforehand), and Matt had a chair. He could see everything, so the chair was probably there in case he felt queasy.

Time was really distorted and I've lost big chunks of what happened. I was chatting to Matt when I looked down and there was this blue bottom with its legs tucked underneath coming out of me. After going on and on to the theatre staff about how this is a sacred event and I don't want them to joke or laugh or tell me the sex of the baby, I exclaimed: "Oh my god, it's a turkey!" Then all went blank until I heard the doctors saying "Look, look, look" and I looked and there was this little blue alien hovering above her mother ship. She'd been eased out and turned over so her arms and legs were stretched out towards me. She squeaked once, opened her eyes and looked straight at me. "It's a little girl", I cried "She's beautiful!" All along, I'd thought she was a boy and had called her a "him", yet she was a lovely little girl!

All went blank again. I guess the doctors cut the cord, and then Evie was immediately put on me. Less than a minute after she'd been born, I was holding her. And there she was, my little angel lying on my chest, right up to my neck as there was so little room with all the cloth and tubes, but we were skin to skin, mummy and baby, and it was the most perfect intimate moment. I kissed her and loved her and talked to her. We had some amazing exchanges in those few minutes, and I'll love that time forever. It was magical.

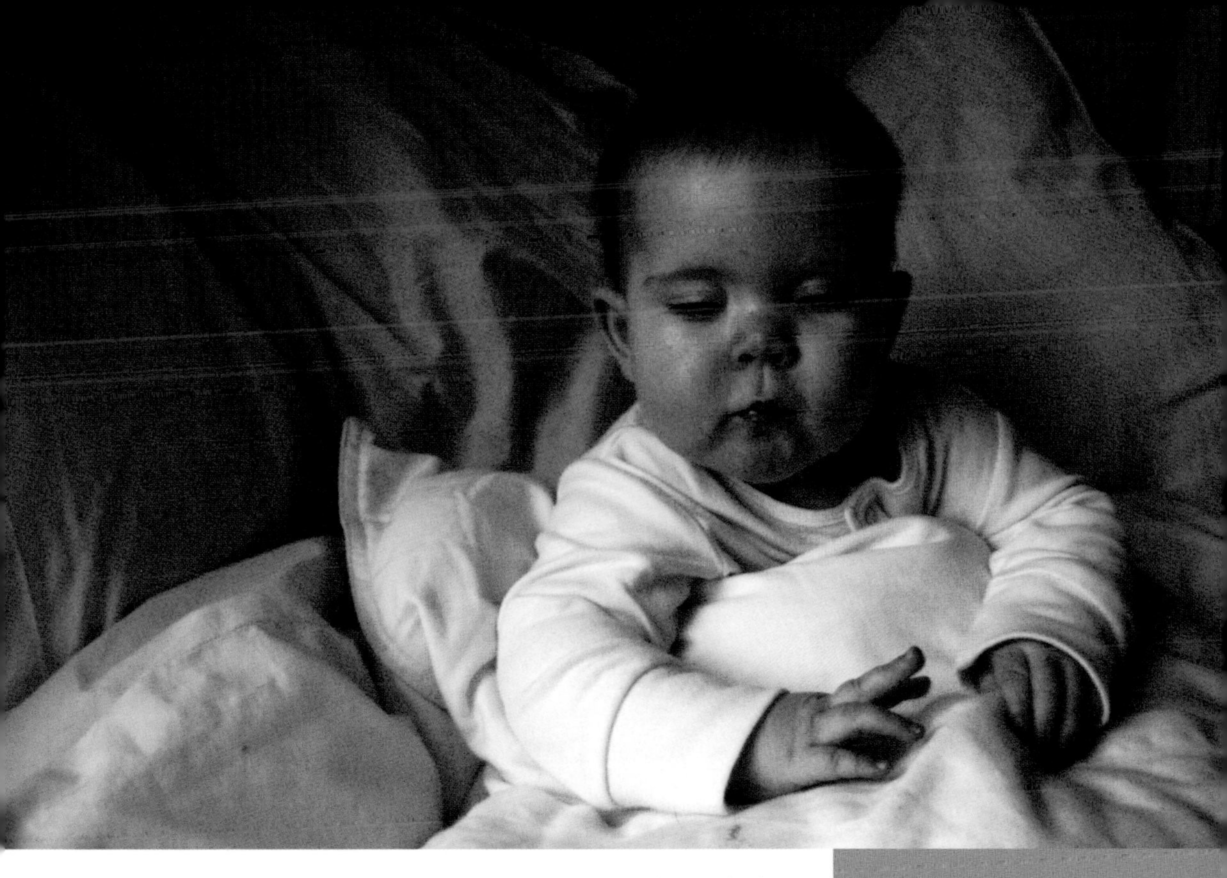

All the turmoil of not having a natural birth was behind me. I had my baby girl in my arms, she was perfect, and she was healthy. She was everything.

I held my baby for some time, and then my midwife put a nappy on her and wrapped her up. She didn't clean or wipe her, just as I'd requested. I held her again, and then Matt took her to the delivery room while I was being wheeled behind them.

The baby was put straight to my breast with the help of a nurse. She sucked immediately and ferociously. My parents came in: "It's a little girl", I echoed. After having three grandsons by my sister, their faces were a picture.

Matt named her Evie Grace, which I found out only after he'd sent an email to all my friends on my behalf.

Our first hours

Later in the evening, when Evie's new extended family had gone, Matt and I just stared at her. After Matt went, it was just my girl and me for the first time. We were in awe of each other, taking each other in. I kept feeding her as she wanted it, those precious drops of colostrum setting her up for life.

Then a nurse came by and told me to put Evie in her cot before I went to sleep. I said I wouldn't. After a few exchanges of words, she smiled and said "We used to encourage mothers to sleep with their babies until someone dropped theirs on the floor".

Throughout that first night we barely slept. Partly because of all the other babies crying for their mummies warmth, and partly because we were so busy loving each other.

And that's the birth of Evie. It's not how I'd dreamed — I'd gone from wanting to give birth unassisted under a tree to having an elective c-section in a few very difficult moves. But I don't regret my decision. The ultimate aim is a healthy baby: how you get there in a situation like this has to always be the choice of the mother.

I haven't a clue what would have happened if I'd attempted to birth Evie naturally, but when I look at how healthy and happy she is I feel that there was a higher source guiding me to elect for a c-section. Contrary to what some natural parents would say, just because someone elects for a c-section (whatever the reason), the mother and child relationship isn't invalidated. They can still go on to live a natural and loving life, as Evie and myself are doing every day. Though I'm often anti-doctors, you have to know when to accept medical help and when not to. Life isn't black and white. My birth story is as special and valid as anyone else's, and I love to share it and relive it.

Our first months

Evie's diet in the first three months was breastmilk, breastmilk and more breastmilk. I flowed over with abundance for my sweet suckling. I also flowed over with prolactin, the mothering hormone, and carried Evie with me everywhere I went. When I worked on my computer (fitted with a big Tachyon disc) she'd lie asleep on my lap. In fact I was back at work two days after the birth — work being next door to my bedroom. I fully appreciated my work at home environment, as I didn't have to separate myself from my baby.

Such a life change

A couple of weeks after having Evie we uprooted and moved to Matt's flat in Bedford. I wasn't ready to live in a new town with a new baby and up two flights of stairs. I was so overweight from eating cooked food that I wasn't strong enough to drag the pram upstairs. Plus it was the summer and there was no garden for my newborn to enjoy.

I'd frequently go back home to Cambridge. My house was for sale but was getting very little interest. Matt said to me that I shouldn't sell as there was a chance we wouldn't end up together. I'd pine for a life, a boyfriend that loved me and a proper family environment for Evie. Everybody kept telling me to give Matt time to get used to being a father, and that he'd show an interest in me again, but it never happened. It wasn't Evie, he adored her. It was me. It didn't matter what I did, nothing changed.

In fluffy mummy mode one minute, I'd visit expensive show homes in the country and dream about our poppet growing up amongst the hollyhocks and babbling brooks with a mummy and daddy to dote on her. In turbulent Kali mode the next, I'd trash Matt's flat, screaming and exhausting myself even further, just wanting some recognition from him, some acknowledgement of my existence. I had one wish — to keep my family together. However, over the months, as Matt slept in a different room, as he went out at night, as he started flirting with other women, and as he continually rebuked me, I knew that I'd soon be a single mother. I knew that my dreams and hopes of Evie growing up in her own nuclear family would be shattered. But I wasn't ready for it, I was really scared and felt more alone than ever in a strange town, with a strange man, with a new baby.

Over the months I'd gone from being feeling a complete woman to feeling totally empty. I was on autopilot as New Year came and went. I stared blankly as the geese in Bedford's River Ouse waddled by. I fed Evie, I loved her, I cherished her but my mind was in other places. I knew that I'd have find a way of living alone with Evie.

Seven months after Evie was born I started to think about feeding her something other than breastmilk.

One day, just after I'd sold my house and around the time of the Spring Equinox, I was walking through Bedford town centre to go to a mother and baby group. It had been such beautiful weather, though I barely noticed it being stuck in a flat. Suddenly a monk approached me. You know the kind, they give you a book on yoga and ask for a donation. Seeing this monk, a very beautiful man, switched something on inside me. What was I doing trying and trying and trying to stay in a situation that was so dysfunctional, twisting me up, altering my perception, when I needed to be around people who let light flow through them, like this guy? I realised that there was no light in my life with Matt, and that we had to alter it there and then or go our separate ways.

Seeing the light

I took my shoes off. I felt the earth, which was great after living in a flat. And I walked on the ground all the way to the mother and baby group. I was shaking. I realised I had to be around people who shine, just like the monk did.

That evening I texted Matt. "I'm optimistic about the future". He texted back "I'm not. I can't see how anything's going to work out". There was my answer. I had a glass of wine to steady my nerves.

When Matt came home that night, Evie was asleep. I gave Matt one more chance, or I was leaving and taking Evie with me. He just couldn't go near me; he couldn't be my boyfriend. My hopes of raising Evie in a family environment had just crumbled beneath my feet. We went upstairs and looked at Evie. I wondered why I repelled men so much. I thought I must be so ugly, or offensive in some way. I left that night with Evie.

Evie got ill, probably as a result of breastfeeding wine and my stress. I went back to stay at Matt's flat for a while until Evie was better, but I never again tried to make it work with him. I had to look forward to a life with just Evie and me.

All by ourselves

At first I was relieved, though I still shouted a lot at Matt. I'd cry at night in bed with Evie. I wasn't lonely but I needed comforting, and the only person who was there was Matt — which wasn't the best solution. Matt said to me, "You're a free spirit trapped in a world full of prisoners". Maybe I am, but I believe that anyone who's trapped has their own key, they just need to remember where they left it. I wished the best for Matt and hope to this day that he finds his key. That'd make his little girl so happy.

At the time I didn't understand why it couldn't work between Matt and me, and I was so scared thinking I'd be a homeless single mum. But at the same time I realised that being without Matt put me in a great position to meet someone who can love me as I need to be loved, which Matt could never do. I realised that I was prepared to compromise so much of myself to be with Matt and keep my family together. I knew deep inside that I would never have been happy with that. Matt did me the biggest favour by being unable to love me, as it stopped me settling for less than I deserve and need. For that, I'm eternally grateful to him, and I now fully understand our sacred contract.

Evie's first food

The stress of this separation was too much for my body to handle. While I somehow managed to carry on working and loving Evie, despite all the confusion and heartache and hormones, my body had had enough. My milk supply decreased. Evie sucked and sucked but got very little out of me. I realised that I had to start her on solids as she needed something inside her. I gave her papaya mixed with a small amount of breastmilk. First she made this face that said "What are you doing to me?" and wouldn't eat it. Then I went to take a spoonful and before I could get it in my mouth she wanted it. She ate it all up! I felt so proud of her for loving her first meal, and thought about how she would soon be a teenager.

Over the next few days I gave Evie pure water. I loved her. I let her suck my booboos despite the fact that little came out. I gave her small amounts of other mushed up food. Thankfully the milk drought only lasted a week or so, but it got Evie weaned quickly onto other foods. As my breastmilk increased again, so did Evie's intake — she was drinking more than ever. She also loved the new flavours I was introducing to her. Spirulina with mango. E3Live with avocado. Banana. Oh, banana. That one wasn't so good. She became constipated and got a bleeding bottom from it. I cut down on the banana from then on and she was fine. I pureed everything I could get my hands on from the raw fruits, vegetables and sea greens that I knew. Evie loved them all, alongside her breastmilk.

Over the next few weeks, my feelings of sickness and worry subsided. I started to make it through the day without crying. I wondered how I'd ever live alone with Evie, how I'd get back in the housing market, how I'd manage to make even a phone call if no-one was there to take Evie just for five minutes. I wondered and wondered. I found some strength that I didn't know I had. Each time you have trauma and turmoil in your life you can either be a victim or a victor, and I realised long ago that my victim days were over.

For the next few months we lived partially at my parents' and partially at Matt's until I somehow managed to get a hefty mortgage and find a beautiful house not far from where I lived before. I really wanted to be close to my friends in Cambridge, to not be so distant from my family and to feel supported. I was completely broken at this time. I'd gone from having a six year period of self-discovery to feeling worthless, unattractive and useless. If it wasn't for Evie I'd have dug a hole and crawled inside. It seemed like the depression I knew before I went raw had come back bigger than ever, though I didn't realise it at the time.

Our sanctuary

Thankfully Evie was there, every day, all day. She was a little bundle of light, an angel, a beautiful treasure, and I loved her. I loved everything about her. Our new home was a sanctuary and I loved it dearly. I felt like I'd been transported from a war zone into peacetime, and I had my poppet with me, which was the most important thing in my life.

I'd gone from shouting at Matt every night to being at peace. I remedied the house's awful decor by having it all stripped and painted white with Ecos paint. I thought of the Imagine video by John Lennon. My home looked like a place of worship, which I probably needed to retrieve my soul.

Sometimes Evie wouldn't sleep and I'd get angry and shout at her. I can count those times on one hand but they cut deep, even now. I love this child, and yet after hours and hours of sucking and kicking and biting and no sleep, even I got worn down by it — just sometimes.

The first year in my new home was eventful with Evie. I was still emotionally turbulent, but every day seemed to get easier. My business started taking off and I had no more financial pressures. I employed a live-in help, Annette, for a while, which was great in many ways. I went out three whole times without Evie in her first eighteen months. I knew I'd soar again one day, but I didn't realise it'd take so long.

A natural child

Evie's increasing raw food diet was part of a whole health package I'd worked out for her. She hasn't been poisoned by vaccinations. Instead I opted to breastfeed her full-term for maximum immunisation benefits. Warm healing herbal teas and anti-viral mushroom extracts also fitted into her diet. I vowed that I'd continue this until she was at least two years old so her immune system would function well for the rest of her life. Evie never needed to go to the doctors. She was extremely healthy and bright. I knew she'd have absorbed a lot of the emotional turbulence I'd experienced with her dad, and so I hoped her wonderful diet and better lifestyle could offset that to some extent.

We rested and recuperated at our new home. Annette made nut mylks, green juices and lunches for us most days. Evie ate sporadically, like any typical toddler. She was still breastfed, still about 50 percentile on the height and weight charts (as she had been at birth), and looked perfectly healthy to me. I continued sleeping with her, bathing with her, and being with her as much as I could.

Child care

When Evie started sleeping less, around the fourteen month mark, I had to make the decision to put her in a nursery for nine hours a week. This was hard for me because she'd be exposed to adults who say things like "Ooh, stinky poo" and other unconscious remarks. But with her ever increasing energy and my need to work at least some of the time, it was the best solution I could come up with. I knew that those hours weren't enough to create a separation between us, but they were enough to enable me to run my business. Of course, I cried the first few times. Evie actually really loved it, and enjoyed hanging out with the other toddlers so much.

The nursery did "messy play" with foods such as puffed rice. On the days that Evie went to nursery they'd do messy play with bubbly water or shredded paper, which was really kind of the staff. Sometimes the nursery would make cakes with the children, with Evie watching over proceedings from her high chair. I was grateful for their thoughtfulness, but realised it made Evie feel different, even at that young age. It did more than just play on my mind.

Well-meaning strangers

Until the age of two Evie was still all-raw, all vegan. Except once. That once happened a few weeks before Christmas when I was in a restaurant having a cuppotea. A well-meaning waiter was playing with Evie, then all went quiet as they had ducked behind the till area. My motheradar tuned in immediately. "You're not feeding her, are you?" I enquired. "Oh, just a little pancake" said the waiter, thinking he was doing good things. Maybe he was on some level, but after seeing the ingredients, animal fat being one of them, I felt sad for Evie as she didn't know what had just gone inside her. I also felt sad for the waiter as he didn't know why I didn't want her to take his gift. I tried to explain, and advised him that in these days of allergies and special diets, it's wise to ask. Evie was sick later that day, and all he'd fed her came right back up. She was rarely sick.

A few days later someone offered Evie cooked chocolate and crisps, but by that time I was wise and ready for pre-mastication intervention. Isn't it odd that people think they're being kind to a child by feeding it trans-fats, wheat and refined sugar?

Christmas with a one-year-old

Annette left the house to return to London. Christmas came. We spent the day with Matt. Christmas for me has always been a time to relax, wind down, enjoy the festivities and enjoy the lack of work and rushing about.

It's so true that Christmas is better with children. For some years before Evie came along, I hadn't even put a tree up. Evie was sixteen months old that year, and she knew things were happening but didn't know what. She wasn't at the stage to ask for things, apart from "That" and "There". I was thankful that I had yet to experience the consumerist and peer-pressure side of Christmas! Evie's continual prodding and carrying of the presents before Opening Day made me laugh. She's a magpie at the best of times, and I can't imagine what was going through her little head when all these sparkly things appeared and she could touch them and move them but not open them. The tree was also a source of amusement. Being a bit of a minimalist with my house, I had a white fibre optic tree. She loved it as the bright tips changed colours. Evie became very excited at tree-turning-on time. She didn't like it when it was time for the tree to go night nights for a year.

Just before Christmas one of the nursery staff asked me to alter one of Evie's days as they were due to hold their Christmas party when she'd normally be there. "There'll be food everywhere", they stated.

So I altered the day. Evie knew nothing different. I told Evie's dad. "How sad" he proclaimed. I soothed him, saying that it may be sad for us, but Evie wouldn't notice. She wouldn't have a clue that she was missing a party. I also said that we'd had a really special raw food gourmet evening party for my customers and colleagues the week before and she loved that. When you're that age, you get what you get, and you don't miss what you don't get. I knew it wouldn't always be that way but I was glad it was there and then.

A new reality

Evie was easy as a baby. I could meet all her needs quickly and simply. Attaching your baby to you at all times enables this to happen with such ease, and I can't understand why anyone would want to do it any other way. The only weird thing about Evie was that as she became a toddler she'd be really clingy and scream at me in the mornings. I didn't know what this was. It could have been residual tension from my split with her dad, or it could have been hunger as I was trying to prepare her breakfast, or it could have simply been "I need cuddling now", which was impossible as I was preparing her breakfast. Wearing Evie in a sling was fine as a baby, but as a toddler, she'd just wriggle and it'd hurt my back, so I gave up at that point.

Another observation came when Evie started to socialise a bit more. When she was with other children, she'd stick with them, play with them, hang out with them and only come to me for her booboo or if she hurt herself. Alone, she clung to me like a shipwrecked koala. With others she roamed free with a smile on her face and anticipation in her heart. It was lovely to see this and yet it broke my heart at the same time: I so wanted Evie to be part of a family — not just me and her. It wasn't fair on her to rely on me to be her mother, carer, feeder and plaything. It wasn't right. It wasn't what other animals did. Children learn from children as much as they learn from adults. They need each other. I started pining for a man to come into my life, to create a family with me for Evie. To give Evie what I thought she deserved, what she'd been denied. But no-one came, the Universe obviously had other plans.

I knew the peace of a short break would bring me some resolve, and it did. This is what happens when you just stop for a second: life comes in. I had an epiphany about how to resolve my lack of family life for Evie.

For years I've thought about living in a community. I've come close to doing it several times, but something has always stopped me. Yet here I was, realising that this was the way forward, and it was workable. I didn't know where or when but I knew that I wanted to put us in an environment where we had love all around us from other natural-living types. I was so excited by this. I had no idea how it would actually manifest, but I did know it was going to happen. It had to.

Children are so precious, and if we want to see ours grow up happily and well rounded then we can't keep them away from other kids. The children in my street are brought up in the "average" way. They cry themselves to sleep, they're fed food-drugs, they're put in child-prison five days a week, they watch brainwashing television and they play video games. Not only couldn't I do that to my angel, I couldn't have her play with these mites, as they'd have nothing in common. They'd end up being a unsuspecting bad example to Evie, and I'd have a fight on my hands at all times. That's not what living a conscious life is about. I was convinced of my grand plan, a plan bigger than any I'd ever made before. I often think the world isn't big enough to hold me, and Evie is also larger than life. Together we can do anything. I was sure that I was going to create an environment that gave Evie the perfect mix of nature, freedom, friends and security.

So I decided to spend the next few years working on myself. I had to be strong if I was to live in a community. I kept the faith and held that dream in my heart. I also put my house up for sale and trusted that it would sell when the time was right.

Appreciating my miracle

It's hard to comprehend how much love a mother has for her child before you're in that situation. You think you know, as you see mothers doing all kinds of irrational things for their children. But as soon as you're a mother your emotions are transmuted into some kind of pure white light that shines permanently onto your child. You would do anything for them.

My life with Evie has been one of wonderment. I love being with her and have consistently felt hormonally driven to do all the things that feel right in my heart. I've really enjoyed discovering her needs through my intuition. The large amounts of prolactin have caused me to temporarily mother everyone else in my life, too, which has altered all my relationships. People come and go in our lives, yet we are each other's constants. I can't imagine life without her now, but in April 2006 the unthinkable almost happened.

When something tragic or life-threatening occurs, and you're not prepared for it, you go directly into autopilot. There's no time to go to pieces, or to think the worst, or to make the wrong decision. You do what you feel instinctively driven to do.

Before Evie was one she ate no nuts, then she had them crushed or chewed by me. Then at around twenty months, she started eating them whole. She asked for them like that, and I felt she was ready to eat them.

Late one afternoon she coughed a little when eating some pine nuts. Then she went to sleep. As she normally doesn't sleep until about 10pm I was just glad of the time off. The next day she was still, but with her eyes open, and she didn't do anything all day. To cut a very long story short, she'd inhaled a pine nut. Because she didn't actually choke on it, it had taken me days to realise that her illness wasn't just a cold, but could have been related to the time she coughed on the pine nut. My mind would jump from "It's just a cold" to "She's got a nut in her lung". She developed pneumonia and we ended up spending four days in hospital with her on an IV antibiotic drip. Under a general anaesthetic she had her lung vacuumed and washed out. We were lucky that her lung hadn't collapsed. We were lucky that it hadn't obstructed her breathing.

For the next eight months I reverted to chewing all Evie's nuts for her and then spitting them into her mouth.

A blissing in disguise

As it turns out the whole nut episode was a blissing in disguise, because Evie's blood tests showed that she was anaemic. This shocked me because I was so careful with her diet, and I knew it contained enough iron. Iron is a weird one though because it's an oxidiser. Evie has a diet very high in antioxidants, which inhibit the absorption of this essential mineral.

Evie was prescribed a sugar-filled iron supplement by the hospital. To avoid conflict with the authorities, I gave it to her for the required time and adjusted her diet. Then I put Evie on Water Oz ionic iron supplement and continued to give her lots of iron-rich parsley. Standard iron supplements, such as the one she had, are about 3% absorbable. Ionic iron is unique in that it's almost 100% absorbable. This means you need much less ionic iron to achieve the same results. You also don't need the associated proteins to take up the iron.

A few weeks later we had a check up with the dietician. It started off strangely and ended up plain surreal. She suggested I feed Evie Nesquik flavoured soya milk and cereals. I couldn't understand why, and our conversation didn't help.

The dietician weighed and measured Evie and discovered that she'd put all her weight back on from when she was in hospital. She was 83cm (at nearly 22 months), which is just under the 50 percentile line. The dietician was pleased. "She's just below average on both, so that's pretty good." I questioned her. "But that's a bottle-fed baby chart, isn't it?" "Yes, the new breastfed charts aren't in use yet." "So she's probably not just below average, is she?" "Well, no. She seems to be doing really well. Bottle fed babies *are* bigger. Yes, she's doing good. But the new breastfeeding charts only go up to a year." This astounded me. The new charts go up to a year, then toddlers and older kids are suddenly measured against children that were bottle-fed as babies. Won't this make them look like their growth has slowed or stunted, jumping from one chart to another? The words "Failure to progress" ran through me, as I imagined the consequences of such medical silliness.

The dietician asked me to list a typical day of Evie's diet. I'd written down her diet the day before and reeled that off to her, in no particular order. She said she'd be able to get it analysed and give me a rough estimate of what's going on in there. I asked how would they count the breastmilk as we don't know how much she gets. "We won't include the breastmilk" "So it won't be very accurate, will it?" I asked. If she was drinking cow milk, they'd include it, but not the breastmilk, not the milk she's designed to have. "Does she drink for a long time?" "No, only about five minutes." "She's probably not getting many nutrients, then. It's if she drinks for 20-30 minutes that she'll get the hind milk." "She drinks me dry every time, so she's getting all that's there. Doesn't the milk change with the age of the baby? Doesn't it become more nutrient dense as they get older?" "Er, I think it does." At this point I think we both realised that we lived in completely different nutritional worlds.

During our conversation, I realised something really important — no-one in our society gets everything they need naturally any more because our food is too deficient these days. As so much "staple" food is fortified, those who eat that type of food get by. Those of us who don't eat it may not be so lucky. This isn't about food groups, calorie counting or restrictive diets. Our food is no longer nutritious enough to support us without us resorting to supplementation — vegan or not. I'd much rather give Evie a good quality supplement, for those few nutrients that are harder to find, than see her eat Coco-Pops and Nesquik. I love Evie too much to feed her anything like that.

Evie's iron levels normalised and I kept her on four teaspoons of ionic iron a day. I saw a few changes after her iron levels came up. I wouldn't have thought there was a problem before she was tested, but she became more independent, much less clingy (she no longer screamed for breakfast), and she grew a lot quicker, hitting 95 percentile at one point. She'd always been about average for her age (measured against artificial-milk fed babies), but since having extra iron, she really did sprout.

She's a big girl now

In addition to ionic iron I gave Evie Blue Manna, which claimed to offer her a full daily RDA of vitamin B12. I also put Water Oz's Water of Life in her drink. This is a supplement that contains all of the known minerals in a concentrated ionic dose. Her bone formula supplement contains vitamins D and K2, but she developed a cavity at three and a half, so I added in more of these two vitamins. The minimum RDA for vitamin D is 400iu. Evie has an average intake of 2000iu. There is no official RDA for vitamin K2, but Evie now has about 200% of the manufacturer's daily value. She hasn't since developed any more cavities. More recently, I added nanotechnology vitamin B12 to Evie's daily supplements. I've always been careful to supplement with vitamin B12, but absorption rates are low when using traditional supplements and I wanted to ensure her vitamin B12 levels were OK.

As Evie grows up she remains curious about food. She's never stuck to one thing, but has had "fussy" times. I regard these as times that she needs a certain nutrient abundant in the food she's eating in excess. For example, she can eat many tomatoes for weeks, and then not touch them for weeks. She does the same with avocados, nuts, peppers, spinach and cucumber. I respect her wishes, always serving the food she's asking for alongside other foods. She then has the choice to fulfil her needs and experiment without pressure. As long as she has her green juice and supplements most days, the rest of her food choices are hers. I only ever restricted her food when she was younger and ate too many nuts because they made her poo really acidic. Other than that I let Evie lead the way with her food. She hasn't been corrupted by human thoughts and preconceptions like I have. Children are our biggest teachers, and I'm very glad I have Evie to teach me — she's amazing.

My breastfeeding career

As a child breastfed on cue, Evie always had access to the best food on the planet. I made sure my diet remained as optimal as possible, though sometimes the stress wore me down and I'd become unconscious about my food choices.

Over time my breastmilk naturally decreased in volume. Evie didn't like water when she was younger, and as my milk supply became less abundant around the age of eighteen months she'd tug at my breasts until I was in a lot of pain. I thought my pleasurable breastfeeding days were at an end as I'd cry in agony, wanting to give Evie more than I had. I started to dread bedtimes as I knew I'd have to endure hours of pain from her sucking my spent boobs. Eventually I got Evie into raw coconut water. Coconuts are the breastmilk of mother earth. They're the only food with lauric acid in them except for breastmilk. They even look like great big boobs, such is the way of the doctrine of signatures. By the age of two Evie was drinking a whole litre of coconut water a day, plus breastfeeding, plus having lots of water-

rich food. I can't tell you how much of a relief to me this was, and it immediately altered our relationship for the better. Bedtimes were transformed into Evie waking up and saying "I want juice!" She'd have her juice and go straight back to sleep — on the breast.

Just before her third birthday, Evie was down to four feeds a day, two of those during the night. At some point just before her fourth birthday my milk had almost dried up, but Evie still was sucking on my breasts to go to sleep. We had a discussion about the day when she would stop breastfeeding. We thought her fourth birthday would be a great time as she'd be a big girl and able to ride a horse. Evie's excitement about riding a horse made the thought of giving up her booboo a little more bearable. During the few months of sucking with no milk, Evie became extremely affectionate to my breasts. She would say "I want to kiss your booboos" and she'd snuggle up to them, kiss them, gently hold them and smile. It was as if she was giving them a huge thank you for all their hard work. This affection carried on until about a month after the breastfeeding stopped.

Unexpectedly, I was very weepy and personalityless once I'd finished breastfeeding. I felt like I had teenage angst all over again. I discovered that there is a condition called post-lactation depression. I took extra DHA, extra vitamin pills, slept lots (Evie's Daddy looked after her a few extra nights), and did some powerful meditations. The outcome was that I felt more powerful, able and ecstatic than before. By looking after myself properly, I'd lost all signs of post-lactation depression within 48 hours of realising that I had it.

Breastfeeding full term wasn't easy for my breasts. The stress of becoming a single mum altered my milk supply, and continuing stress caused them to dry up when other mums can breastfeed as long as the child wants. But Evie has had four years of mummy's milk, perfect intimacy, love hormones and the best food ever on tap. We both feel complete at the end of this chapter of our lives.

Veggan?

Researching this book has given me the opportunity to reconsider some of my previous beliefs. It's very easy for an adult to supplement herself, and to know if she doesn't feel right, but it's different for a child. As Evie turned four, I was tiring of chasing her around the house with supplements and I was frustrated by the incomplete information distributed by vegan "authorities". None had ever mentioned the importance of vitamin K2 for bone and tooth health. I hadn't seen any life-long raw vegan children who looked healthy, and the words of my friend Tish rang through my ears. "It's normally when breastfeeding finishes that deficiencies start to show." Evie has had the most wonderful nutritional start in her life, yet as she finished breastfeeding my intuition was screaming at me to introduce some kind of animal by-product into her diet, and to make her life easier when eating with others.

With this in mind, even though I'm a long-term vegan, I eventually decided to give Evie 1-3 organic free-range egg yolks a week. With natural vitamins K2 and D, it felt right adding this tiny amount of animal by-product to her diet. I would be happier if the chickens were rescued and living on my land, and it's looking like I'll get there with that very soon.

I also dropped the amount of raw food she eats to around 80%, the rest being foods such as rye bread, hummous, buckwheat pasta and small amounts of potatoes. It's very easy for me to get supplements and ecstatic foods into these cooked dishes, because she sees the food as a treat and so eats it all up. I always put something raw with it, too, even though she insists on having "just pasta". Mother has her limits!

These two radical changes don't feel like a compromise. I actually feel like I've enhanced Evie's quality of life. Evie is extremely happy and healthy. She's also a good height (78 percentile on her fourth birthday), unlike so many other raw vegan children I've seen over the years. My feelings about raw food remain unchanged, and if I had another child, I'd raise him almost exactly the same as I did Evie. I'd be extra-vigilant with the supplements and I'd introduce egg yolks at around aged two. I've always been happy with Evie's diet and progress, and I look forward to it continuing to evolve.

Admmm's magic

The only man I'd had in my life since Evie's dad was Admmm. We had a complex on-off relationship for about two and a half years. He would never call me his girlfriend and we both made attempts at going our separate ways because he couldn't commit to me in the way I wanted. From the beginning of 2008, he moved into my house, to help me finish this book. His presence altered Evie and me. I've never met such a gentle, open-hearted and loving being. I've never had so much in common with one person. Evie would act almost like his wife or mother, shouting at him "You're not going to the pub, Adam, get back here now", while chasing him up the road. Their relationship was super-special. Admmm finally experienced a family life and Evie loved the experience of a man about the house.

Admmm always said he was going to move on. "Don't leave me until you find my paradise for me," I'd say. One day, Admmm found a community of co-houses. It was on 23 acres of shared land. I didn't resonate with the house for sale but I fell in love with another one, made of cedar. I wished that house was for sale instead. Two days later, it was. We were all so excited about this house. Admmm was saying how confused he was, that he realised how well we got on and that we had the same vision for a future. I told him that he should go away for a few weeks to see how he really felt about me. I didn't want him to just fall in love with my dream, it had to be more than that.

We all went down south to visit the cedar house but a couple of hours before we were due to visit the land Admmm and I had a misunderstanding, an argument by text that should never have even happened. I left him at his friend's house and went to see the cedar house with Evie. It was perfect. There was even a four-year old girl next door. I was sad about Admmm, we'd been through so much together, but I realised that he wasn't going to move with us. I drove home without Admmm.

A day later Admmm was dead. My beautiful boy, the only man I'd loved in so many years had had an accident and was no longer in his body. I would have done anything to have him back, but he was gone.

Four days after Admmm died, I was questioning my future, even though I couldn't think beyond the next minute. My estate agent rang me. After my house had been for sale for two years, someone had put an offer in. He hadn't even seen it. I can't imagine this all happened by coincidence, and I pictured Admmm's spirit pulling all the strings he could to get me to move, now he'd found me the perfect house. As I write this, my offer on the cedar house has been accepted, so it looks like I'll be moving to the house and community of my dreams.

Admmm led Evie into the paradise and then he found his own paradise. This huge Admmm-shaped hole in our lives is slowly healing. I'm making sure I fill it with love, beauty and awe. I've promised Admmm that I'll raise Evie in the environment she deserves, the environment that he found for us.

The beginning

Evie has continued to flourish. Her psychic abilities and excessive love gene astound me, and I know that the food she eats will keep this part of her open. Too much cooked food and animal food closes us down emotionally, spiritually, physically and psychically. In contrast, raw plant food creates ecstatic beings of all of us. One day, all children will be given optimal food from birth but at the moment this is almost unprecedented in our society.

I have no idea how Evie will turn out because I don't know of any other children raised on raw foods and ecstatic foods who are now adults. All I know is that she won't turn out obese, ill, depressed or spotty. I can guess that she'll turn out radiant, happy, beautiful and living the life of a divine being, which surely is everyone's birthright.

Alchemy tools

To make great raw food easily, you may need a few tools that the average kitchen doesn't boast.

Dehydrator —The dehydrator acts like a low-temperature oven, blowing warm air via a fan over the food. The food then dries out over time to create biscuits, burgers, dried fruits and vegetables, cakes, pizzas, crackers and breads. I dehydrate at around 115 degrees Fahrenheit or 46 degrees Celsius. If the food is quite thick, I'll crank it up a little for an hour or so. If it's quite thin, I'll reduce the temperature. You can place solid ingredients onto the trays, but liquid ingredients need to be poured onto sheets that line the trays. Once the food has set, you can peel off the sheet and reuse it indefinitely. My favourite brand for a large kitchen is the Excalibur. If you have a smaller kitchen, try the Stockli, as it's more compact, but you can stack as many extra trays as you like.

Blender —A high-power blender can make flour out of seeds and grains, and it'll purée everything that you throw into it. That's how we make such smooth soups and patés. I use the Vita-Prep 3, which is a commercial blender. If you can't get a Vita-Prep, then find the best blender available to you. It won't be able to achieve the same consistency as a Vita-Prep but your food will still be lovely! If you don't have a Vita-Prep and there is no liquid in the recipe you're making, then you can use a food processor or hand blender instead. For your baby's first foods, a hand or wand blender will be invaluable to you.

Food Processor — I use the Magimix 5000, which has an attachment for making crisps, fine and coarse graters, and several bowl sizes. For your baby's first foods you can find mini food processors that finely chop or blend tiny amounts of food.

Juicer — I don't use my juicer as much as my Vita-Prep, but it's still great for the kitchen. A good masticating juicer will cost a small fortune but it should last a lifetime. My favourite is the Green Power Kempo as it uses magnetic and infra-red technology to keep the juice fresher for longer. We also use a citrus juicer, and frequently enjoy freshly squeezed orange juice with some green powder added to it.

Fridge — One is never enough, and big could always be bigger. And you may need to pay someone to clean it out for you on a regular basis.

Sprout bag or nut mylk bag — Probably one of the cheapest and most versatile additions, even a pop sock will do. Use to strain juices, to sprout seeds and to make mylks and cheezes.

Spirooli or spiraliser — This is a gadget that makes "spaghetti" out of courgettes, squash, mooli and other hard vegetables. I prefer the spirooli, as it's easier to use and makes slightly wider strands.

Vegetable peeler — this is a standard piece of equipment but I mention it here because it's great for making strips out of vegetables. Use it for slicing the length off a cucumber or courgette, then roll it up with paté for an instant and beautiful treat.

Alchemical ingredients

You will be familiar with most of the fresh foods that I use in this book. I've also outlined our favourite ecstatic foods and sea vegetables earlier in the book, so you may be wondering what else you may need to fill your cupboards with. Here's a list of some ingredients that may be new to you. It goes without saying that I only look for organically certified or wild food, but I've said it anyway.

Powdered green superfood — I add a touch of one of these to most of our soups and savoury dishes. Pure Synergy and Nature's Living Superfood are the two brands I prefer. I also use powdered hemp leaf. If you're organised you can harvest weeds, dehydrate them, powder them and store them for future use.

Carob powder — This is sweeter than cacao powder and higher in calcium. It works well with cacao as that contains lots of magnesium. We use raw carob powder, which is unroasted and untoasted.

Oils — All the oils I use are cold pressed and come in dark glass bottles. Coconut oil solidifies when it's cold. Cacao butter has a slightly higher melting temperature, and is harder when solid. Keep oils that solidify out of the fridge, in a cool, dark cupboard. Never eat them if they taste rancid. Keep oils such as hemp, pumpkin and flax in the fridge, along with Udo's Choice. When I use cacao butter and coconut butter, I melt them at a very low heat. I use a pan and keep the flame low, stirring often. As soon as melting is underway, I remove it from the heat and let it continue melting on its own.

Nuts — Most commercial nuts are heated at a low to moderate temperature before being packaged. It's good to forage for fresh nuts where possible. Cashew nuts, unless "really raw," are heated to above 60 degrees Celsius in the process of removing them from their shells. Really raw cashew nuts are expensive but taste very different, and give really creamy results in recipes.

Nut butters — Everyone's heard of peanut butter but these days it's possible to get all manner of delicious nuts and seeds ground to a smooth butter. My company Detox Your World produces Hempini (hemp seed butter), Tahini (sesame seed butter), and White Almond butter. Too moreish for little fingers!

Olives — You can buy certified raw olives, which are free from processed salt and other additives. I love to add shavings of Peruvian sundried olives into our meals or dressings. If you find yourself with olives covered in processed salt, then rinse, soak and drain them a few times to remove as much of the salt as possible. Take care when giving olives to a child, as they may contain stones or stone fragments.

Salt — Evie has never tasted table salt. It's highly refined, mineral-deficient and toxic. We enjoy Himalayan pink salt, Celtic sea salt and salty flavours such as seaweeds and celery.

Sprouts — We eat many sprouts, and our favourites are alfalfa, broccoli, leek and sunflower. They liven up casseroles, sandwiches, salads and soups. They are easy to grow, and the seeds cost pennies.

Water — Evie's never drunk water straight from the tap. We have a filter that balances the pH, ionises it and filters it. It fits onto the tap and enables us to rinse all our food in filtered water. Before this, I'd buy bottled water and would ration it!

He shou wu — Also called Fo Ti, this is an ancient Chinese healing herb particularly favoured by older people and those needing a pick-me-up. The Chinese say it's a 'youth-giving tonic' and can even reverse the greying of hair. We love it because it makes us sing and feel ecstatic.

Tamari — This is a wheat-free version of soya sauce, and we think it's much tastier. It's found in most oriental shops, wholefood shops and stupormarkets.

Miso — This is a staple flavouring in Japanese cooking. It is a fermented paste of barley, soya or rice with a distinctive and wholesome taste. It is available as a heavier, richer dark barley variety or a lighter, sweeter variety. It's very versatile, adds another dimension to all our meals, and is great for extra B vitamins. Though it's initially cooked, it's then made "live" with a special fungus culture called koji that ferments and colonises the barley or rice. This is why it's important to always look for the unpasteurised brands: the culture, and therefore the miso, will still be alive.

Mushrooms — With so many varieties at our feet, mushrooms can give us the flavours no other plant-like thing can, but be aware that they often carry other strains of non-beneficial fungi upon them. A thorough rinse in a mild solution of hydrogen peroxide will zap the nasties. There are also many medicinal mushrooms that help improve organ and immune function, such as reishi and shiitake.

Agave nectar — Agave nectar has become a popular low-GI sweetener over recent years, but most supermarket varieties have been cooked to death. Make sure yours is raw and pure — you can certainly taste the difference!

Lúcuma — A very popular fruit in Peru and neighbouring countries — in fact it's their favourite ice-cream flavour. Rich in antioxidants and vitamin B3, it's a tasty and valuable ingredient. We have it as a powder, and it makes all our sweets really creamy.

Engevita — Engevita yeast is one of the richest natural sources of the B group of vitamins. It is also rich in protein, amino acids, enzymes, minerals and trace elements. Engevita is purely natural, and is a primary grown strain of Saccharomyces Cerevisiae, often called brewer's yeast. We use it in soups and sprinkled on salads, and it really takes Evie's nori rolls to the next dimension.

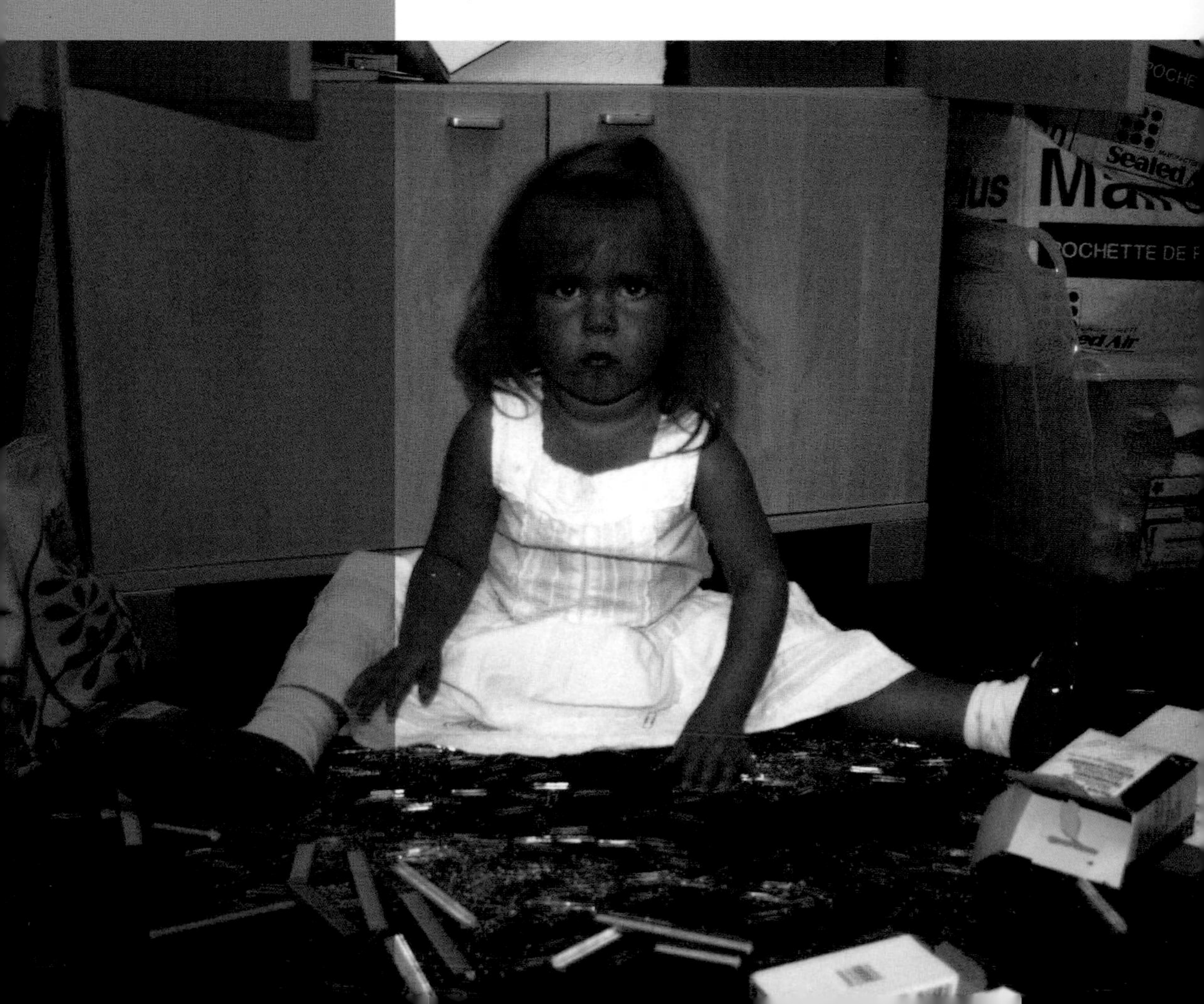

Apple cider vinegar — For centuries the medicinal properties of apple cider vinegar have been passed from old wife to younger wife: great for eating, cleaning, gleaming and making the best dressings ever. By far the best I've ever tasted is Biona's — the only non-pasteurised variety on the market. Taste it and never look back.

Pesto — A key ingredient in normal pesto is parmesan cheese. Luckily there are now a few raw/vegan brands such as Carleys and Sunita. Look out for fresh ones in your local wholefood shop.

Mesquite meal — This is a traditional Native American food produced by gathering ripened seed pods from the mesquite tree and grinding them into a fine powder. This high-protein meal contains good quantities of calcium, magnesium, potassium, iron and zinc, and is rich in the amino acid lysine as well. It has a sweet, rich, molasses-like flavour with a hint of caramel and blends well into smoothies or other drinks, especially those made with cacao and maca.

Apricots — I like to use dried apricots as a sweetener instead of high-sugar dates. I find them more grounding and the taste is more subtle. I always use the brown unsulphured variety.

Purple corn — This corn, although almost identical to its yellow brother, contains substantial amounts of antioxidants and other useful phytochemicals. We use it in food as a powder and dark purple extract and in tea as dried kernels.

Etheriums — The Etherium range is a set of different coloured spiritual supplement powders that originate from ancient riverbeds in Arizona. Many have been clinically shown by the Alpha Learning Institute, USA to affect brain function in different ways, balancing the two cerebral hemispheres and helping to enhance concentration, learning, memory and more esoteric human powers.

Brazilian ginseng — This is one of the most highly revered South American herbs. In the last ten years Brazilian ginseng has become a popular herb amongst Olympic athletes. Its properties help to increase muscle-building and endurance without the side-effects associated with steroids. People wanting to control their blood sugar levels love this food! Those wanting more energy love it! Anyone with hormonal issues loves it. Even those wanting a better sex life love it! We always add some to our chocolates.

Exotic fruits — These days it's possible to buy almost any fruit from any continent at your local ethnic shop. Look out especially for fresh green coconuts, mangosteens, tamarinds, rambutans and the best fruit by far — the durian. Evie and I are both duriaddicts of the highest order.

Enzymes — Enzymes are the 'spark of life'. Without enzymes our bodies do not properly break down food; and we do not absorb vitamins, minerals and amino acids, which are the basis of health. Vegan digestive enzymes can be sprinkled on food to help make it even easier to digest.

Açaí — Jam packed with antioxidants, açaí is a deep purple, delicious-tasting fruit. It is the dark purple skin that contains the anthocyanins (antioxidants) that we need to protect us from our increasingly toxic environment.

Vanilla — This is available in many forms. My favourite by far has to be the pod: look for plump, long ones. It's hard to find them raw, though — most are steamed. Split them down the middle and scrape out the tiny fragrant seeds. It is also possible to buy vanilla extract, a solution containing the flavour compound vanillin. Also available is vanilla essence, a more dubious product potentially containing unnatural flavourings.

Essential oils — These oils are fantastic for flavouring chocolate, cakes and desserts. Bear in mind that they are extremely concentrated products and should be kept away from children until diluted. Some are not suitable for pregnant women or breastfeeders, so check before using. Having said that, we only ever use a few drops in a whole batch of chocolate, so it's rarely an issue.

Salba® — Brand name for a South American strain of the chia seed, Salba is a very rich source of EFAs and is very high in protein, minerals and fibre. It improves bowel function. When ground up it's great as a sticky base for dehydrated foods, similar to flax.

Herbs — Herbs really do add another dimension to any meal and the best thing is you can grow them so easily in your garden or window sill. Fresh herbs are aromatic and heady, while dried herbs are often more pungent.

Transatlantic translations

Many of my books end up in the arms of Americans, so just for them, here's a list of all those quaint English words that they don't use.

Coriander = cilantro
Sharon fruit = persimmon
Spring onions = green onions
Crisps = chips
Rocket = arugula
Beetroot = beet
Clingfilm = saran wrap

Aubergine = eggplant
Courgette = zucchini
Chips = fries
Chick peas = garbanzos
Sweetcorn = corn/maize
Pepper = bell pepper

First foods 6-12 months

Keep breastfeeding on cue throughout this time as your child explores what's to come. If your child doesn't have enough teeth, be careful about serving anything with texture. Always err on the side of caution, and blend, blend, blend!

Continue adding supplements for at least as long as you breastfeed, and start to introduce them to your child in a form and amount that's appropriate for her age.

Try serving these foods with your finger — that way it's more familiar and you'll ensure that you haven't overheated the food in the blender or bain marie (a small bowl of food sat in a larger bowl of hot water).

Introduce one food at a time, leaving a gap of a couple of days between each new recipe to ensure you catch allergies and intolerances early. Blend superfoods into previously introduced foods.

When you introduce seeds and nuts into your child's diet, blend them or ideally chew them up first and pass them from your mouth to hers. The enzymes in your saliva will help break them down and there will be no risk of choking.

Tropical fruit with breastmilk

30g ripe mango, papaya, banana, pineapple or other soft fruit
20ml expressed breastmilk

Infinite tastes with that familiar mummyness. Serves one. Keeps for one day when refrigerated in a sealed container.

Remove any skin, stones or seeds from the fruit. Blend the fruit and milk in a baby food processor and place in the baby's bowl. Warm it for serving by sitting the bowl in a bowl of hot water, and stirring.

Babies can't digest bananas very well, so it's best to chew them first to give them your enzymes, to serve them only really ripe, or to wait until the baby is a year old.

Butternut mash

50g butternut squash
1 teaspoon Udo's choice oil

Peel and seed the squash. Blend the squash until creamy. Mix in the oil and serve.

Sweet potato cake

30g sweet potato
20g courgette

Peel the vegetables. Blend together until creamy and serve.

Baby green juice

Getting your small one used to the taste of greens at a young age is easy with a recipe such as this. Offer small amounts, as you can always freeze leftovers in ice cubes for another day.

Blend all ingredients in a high-speed blender. Strain through a nut mylk bag and serve in a beaker.

100ml water
10g parsley
1 carrot
2 stalks celery

Spiralling out of the car Seat

Blend all ingredients until creamy and serve.

30g cucumber
20g apple
½ teaspoon spirulina

Lettuce pray

Salads are mild and gentle at this stage. Offer with love and gratitude.

Blend everything until creamy and serve.

20g dark lettuce leaves
¼ teaspoon wheatgrass juice powder
¼ avocado
20g tomato

Apricot crumble

Blend everything until creamy and serve.

50g fresh apricot
10g shelled hemp seeds
5ml raw hemp seed oil

1 banana
¼ teaspoon maca powder

Blend both ingredients and then serve.

carob delight

¼ avocado
½ banana
⅛ teaspoon marine phytoplankton
1 teaspoon raw carob powder

Blend all ingredients and then serve.

30g young coconut jelly
10g shelled hemp seeds
5ml Udo's Choice oil

Blend everything until very creamy and serve.

Melon dramatic

50g any melon

Remove any seeds, blend until smooth and serve.

crystalmole with crudités

1 avocado
¼ teaspoon Crystal Manna
Selection of veggies to dip, such as cucumber, carrot, broccoli, cauliflower, courgette, peppers, tomatoes etc

This is a great going-on food for very small kiddies as there are lots of exciting tastes and textures to discover. Serves two. Keeps for one day when refrigerated in a sealed container.

Mash the first two ingredients together and put in a small bowl on a plate. Cut the veggies into thick sticks and arrange on the plate to serve.

Durian

Serve on its own please, ouchy skin and hard stones removed.

crystal tips

A very simple yet pretty dish for the very young crystal child toddler. I don't know where Alistair is. Serves one. Keeps for one day when refrigerated in a sealed container.

- 1 avocado
- 1 teaspoon Crystal Manna flakes

Cut the avocado into eight wedges and dip the tips into a jar of Crystal Manna flakes. Arrange in a pretty way, and watch your toddler enjoy the crystal sparkles!

plum pudding

- 40g fresh plums
- 10g prunes
- ¼ teaspoon purple corn extract

Remove skin and stones from the plums and remove any stones from the prunes. Blend everything until creamy and then serve.

raspberry pudding

- 40g raspberries
- 10g raw tahini
- 10g raw mesquite powder

Blend everything until creamy. Pass through a fine sieve to remove any remaining seeds.

Zebras

1 avocado
1 sheet of nori

This is exciting to serve when babies are slightly older. You can add these to salads, or serve them alone to a young toddler or as a snack. I like to add them to a "field" of sprouts, as it looks like the zebras are grazing. Serves one. Keeps for one day when refrigerated in a sealed container.

Cut the avocado into wedges. Using scissors, cut 5mm x 30mm strips from the nori. Wrap these around the avocados to create stripes. Don't be tempted to use one long strip as this could cause choking. Place the avocados on a plate so they look like zebras.

Coconut Water

Find your way into a fresh young coconut and decant the water into a beaker.

Nightea-night

1 teaspoon dried chamomile flowers or one teabag
50ml water

Boil the water, steep the chamomile until cooled, strain and serve.

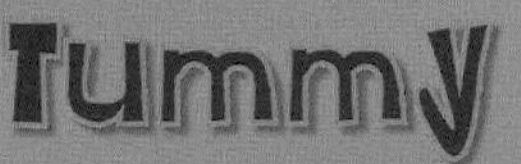

Tummy troubles

1 teaspoon dried peppermint leaves or one teabag
50ml water

Boil the water, steep the peppermint until cooled, strain and serve.

Especially for breakfast

Filling a child's hungry tummy in the morning with tasty, slow-releasing food makes them happy and ready to do very important playing for the rest of the morning.

Bungalow cheeze

100g raw macadamia nuts
½ teaspoon dark miso
5ml Udo's Choice oil
5ml lemon juice
1 capsule digestive enzymes
70ml pineapple juice

Not quite as soft as cottage cheese but very tasty. It goes really well topped on celery or with slices of apple. Serves four. Keeps for up to four days covered in the fridge.

Soak the nuts in water for at least an hour, then discard the water, and rinse. Put everything in a food processor and blend until still chunky, but with a good creamy consistency. You can leave this covered in a warm place for a day or two to ferment the cheeze.

Nectarine sporridge

400ml water
40g Salba or chia
1 nectarine, more for garnish if required

If you blend Salba or chia with water for a fair time, you get a milky or creamy texture. When you add fruit you get a very dreamy start to the day. Serves two. Keeps for two days covered in the fridge.

Blend everything in a high-speed blender until the contents form a milky and totally smooth consistency. This may take a minute or so. Serve with extra nectarine as a garnish.

Holly's strawberry crumble

300g strawberries
125g almonds, soaked overnight
40g raw rolled oats
3 medjool dates
10-20ml raw agave nectar (to taste)
1/8 teaspoon Blue Manna (optional but delicious)

Holly Paige lives in Totnes and is the mother of four children. Three of them are raw vegetarians. She's a beautiful right-brained goddess and I love everything about her – especially her food! That's why I asked her to contribute a recipe. Here's Holly:

We like this dish because it's so homely and "normal", a proper English dessert like something my grandmother in Devon would have made. It's light and balanced but also filling and sustaining. The recipe makes four, which could mean it serves four people or two people get a second helping. We like to eat all our food freshly prepared but it would be fine out of the fridge the next day.

Slice the strawberries and place them in the bottom of a large dish or four individual dishes. Process the almonds, oats, dates and agave nectar together until smooth and crumble over the top. If you're feeling particularly wild, sprinkle a tiny bit of Blue Manna over the top.

Quick mushrooms

4 button mushrooms
¼ teaspoon Seagreens
10ml raw pumpkin seed or hemp seed oil
5ml tamari

Perfect for when your small one wakes up hungry. Serves one toddler; double the quantity for a larger child or make this as a quick starter while you magic up something else. Keeps for two days in a sealed container in the fridge.

Thinly slice the mushrooms (the thinner you slice them, the quicker they'll be ready). Put them into a serving bowl and add the remaining ingredients.

Mix thoroughly, and as you're mixing they'll marinate before your eyes. They are ready in a few minutes.

You can serve them as they are, or add some crackers, vegetable sticks and seeds on the side.

1 cucumber
A filling of your choice, such as guacamole, paté, seed cheese etc
5 olives

This is a filling and easy to eat sarnie that doesn't leave you drowsy like that pesky bread does. To eat it on the go, half wrap it in foil and munch! Serves two. Keeps for one to two days, depending on the filling, in a sealed container in the fridge.

Cut the cucumber in half and scoop out the insides. Chop the olives and mix them with the filling. Spread the mixture on the cucumber halves and put them back together again.

Breakfast bar

Though it's really tart, Evie loves this recipe. When I first made it I thought it'd be a great breakfast on the go for a few days. It would have been, but she ate them all in a day. Makes about twelve bars. Keeps for seven days when refrigerated in a sealed container.

- 200g raw buckwheat
- 150g raspberries
- 50g dried apricots
- 50g raw mesquite powder
- 50g Incan berries
- 50g golden flax seeds
- 40g lúcuma powder
- 5g maca powder
- ½ teaspoon vanilla extract
- ¼ teaspoon Himalayan pink salt

Soak the buckwheat in water for at least 20 minutes. Discard the water, and rinse. Add the buckwheat to a high-speed blender and blend it to a smooth paste.

Grind the flax to a powder and add to a large mixing bowl with all the other ingredients. Mix well by hand until you have a dough, smashing the raspberries but keeping them visible.

On a dehydrator tray lined with a sheet, mould the dough into a 10x20 cm rectangle. Dehydrate at 115°F/46°C for four hours. Flip the whole bar over, cut into fingers without separating, and dehydrate for another two hours. By this time you should be able to separate the fingers and then dehydrate for a final hour before serving or storing.

Buckwheat cereal

1 cup raw buckwheat
2 cups water

Evie loves this on its own. However, the variations are limitless: add chopped fresh fruit, dried fruit, nuts, nut mylk and seeds for countless mueslis. Serves one. Keeps for seven days when refrigerated in a sealed container and rinsed daily.

Soak the buckwheat in the water overnight. In the morning, rinse and serve. If you're in a hurry you can get away with soaking it for just twenty minutes, but it's better if soaked for longer.

Buckwheaties

10 cups raw buckwheat
20 cups water

This stores for ages, so I make a big bowl of it and keep it sealed. It's the best base for any cereal and it's also great in cakes and biscuits. Keeps for over six months when kept in a sealed container.

Soak the buckwheat overnight in the water. Rinse and drain in the morning and leave it to sprout for a day. Rinse it once or twice throughout the day to keep it fresh.

The next day, rinse one more time and then thinly spread the buckwheat out on lined dehydrator trays. Dehydrate for six hours or until crunchy with no moisture left.

Breakfast for friends

When we have people over I make a big platter full of sweet and non-sweet fruits. In the middle I place a dried seed and fruit mix such as Mix of munch**. I also serve lots of herbal tea or hot chocolate. It seems to keep everyone happy and it's easy. Evie loves tucking in with other people, so she eats more at times like this.**

You can use absolutely any fruits; here are some suggestions:

Banana with pear
Raspberries with parsley
Cucumber with red grapes
Vine tomatoes with avocado
Apple with tangerine
Mix of munch
One of the cheeses
Some raw breads and crackers

Butternut tortilla

Evie was so surprised when she tried this. "That's really nice" she said, with a stuffed face. As if I usually make disgusting food. Serves two if you're allowed some. Keeps for three days when refrigerated in a sealed container.

200g butternut squash
30g flax seeds
4 cherry tomatoes
10g parsley
4 olives, pitted
Pinch of Himalayan pink salt

Finely grind the flax seeds. Quarter the tomatoes. Finely chop the parsley. Blend the squash with the flax to form a smooth paste. In a bowl, mix the paste with the tomatoes, olives and parsley. Put a little parsley to one side to garnish.

Flatten the mixture into a thick pancake on a lined dehydrator tray. Sprinkle with the remaining parsley. Dehydrate at 115°F/46°C for about five hours or until you can wait no more.

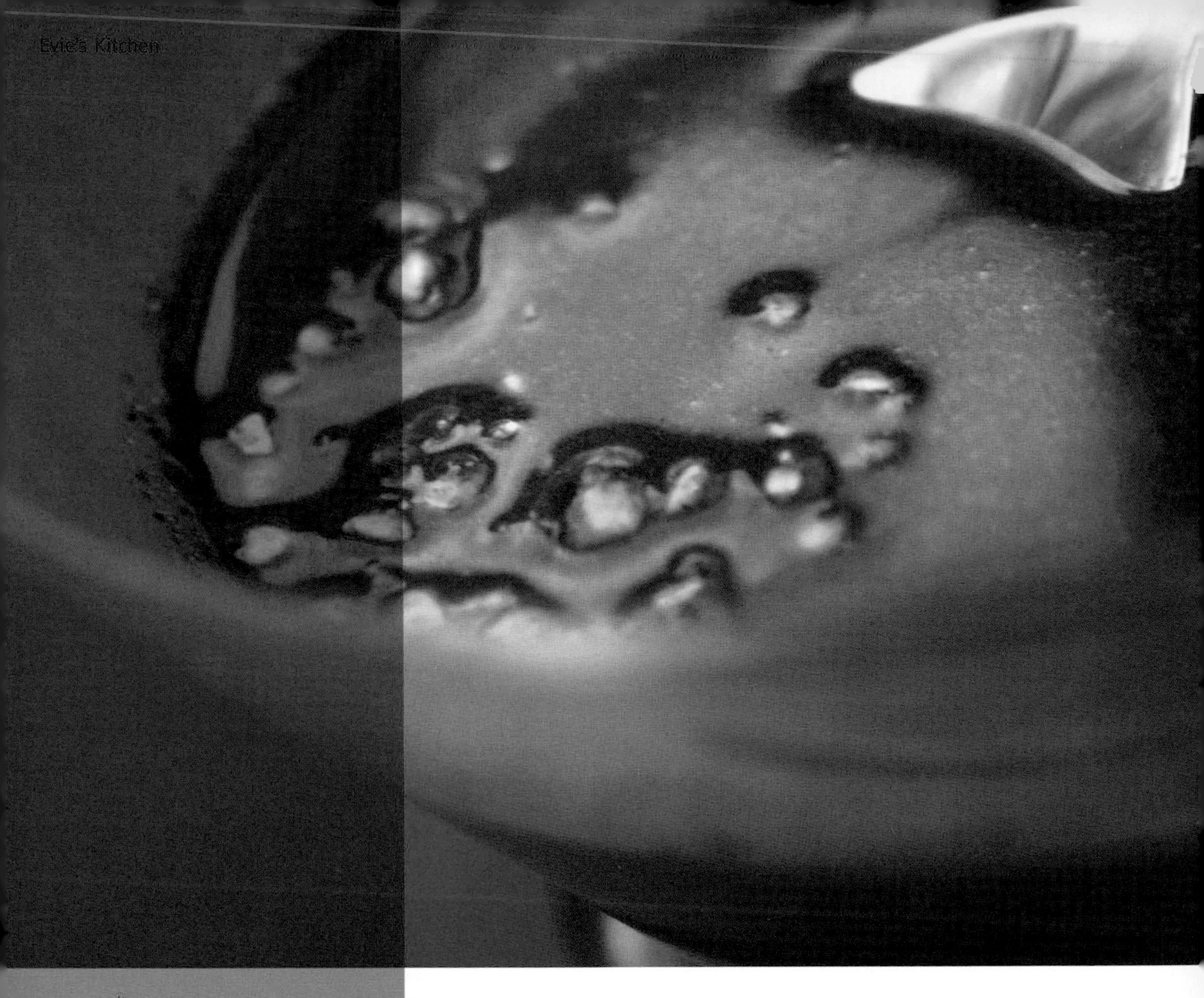

i'd rather have a bowl of cacao drops

100g raw buckwheat
10g lúcuma powder
10g raw cacao powder
10ml raw agave nectar
40ml hand-hot water
½ teaspoon maca
1 Blue Manna capsule

Some commercial cereals are made from by-products of the food industry. Some are full of artificial chemicals, which children really shouldn't be eating. Some are loaded with white sugar, which is too unhealthy to even talk about. This cereal is highly nutritious, sweet and very tasty, with no nasty bits. Hands up who doesn't like chocolate? Serves two. Keeps for two days when refrigerated in a sealed container.

Soak the buckwheat for 20-30 minutes in a pudding bowl of warm (not hot) water (this is not the water in the recipe). Discard the water and rinse the buckwheat.

Empty the contents of the Blue Manna from its capsule. Add all the ingredients to a bowl and mix thoroughly. Eat while still warm.

Muffins W' Stuffin

I was a vegan in the olden days before pizza and muffins were invented, and didn't know what a muffin tasted like. Yet you get this feeling about food, don't you? Even if you've never eaten it. So I set about feeling my way through a muffin recipe. I think I got it right because everyone who tries these says they taste like the best muffins ever! Makes six muffins. Keep for four days when refrigerated in a sealed container.

200g raw mesquite powder
100ml water
100g buckwheat
50ml raw agave nectar
50g golden flax seeds
20ml olive oil
1 apple
1 sweet pear
½ teaspoon cinnamon
Pinch of Himalayan pink salt

Soak the buckwheat in water for twenty minutes, then rinse and strain. Grind the flax to a flour and pour into a large mixing bowl. Grind the buckwheat to a paste and tip into the mixing bowl.

Core and blend the pear and apple to a purée. Put half of this blended mixture and the water into the mixing bowl with all the other ingredients. Reserve the other half of fruit purée. Mix everything until smooth.

Put two teaspoons of the mixture into muffin cases and press down. Make a well with your finger and dollop a teaspoon of the fruit purée into each hole.

Cover each muffin with more muffin mixture until they're full up. Smooth over the tops.

Put in a dehydrator for six hours at 115°F/46°C. Put a small knife down the sides of the muffin cases to prise the muffin away. Turn each muffin over and gently shake to release it from its case. Dehydrate without the cases for a further four hours at 115°F/46°C.

"Children do not have the reserves of adults and have to grow, so it's absolutely essential to provide them with the nutrients that they need. Successfully raising her daughter on raw food has led to Shazzie uncovering invaluable and much needed information about raw nutrition that will be useful to people of all ages who want to follow the raw path healthily and happily." – Holly Paige, mother of three raw vegetarian children

in a jam

50g raspberries
20g goji berries
1 level teaspoon purple corn extract
5ml raw agave nectar

This is great spread on any of the bread recipes. Keeps for about a week if sealed in the fridge. If it goes a bit solid over time, you can water it down.

Soak the goji berries in water for about ten minutes. Drain the berries and use the sweetened water in some other recipe.

Add all the ingredients to a blender and blend until smooth. Spread everywhere and anywhere.

Salbioca

This is very quick and easy to make and hits the sweet spot that children love. Vary the dried fruit to your heart's content. It does actually turn into a tapioca-like substance before your very eyes. Serves two small ones. Keep for four days when refrigerated in a sealed container.

200ml warm water
30g raisins
20g Salba or chia
20g dried apricots
20g dried pear

Finely chop the dried apricots and pear and add to the Salba in a small mixing bowl. Pour over the warm water and stir. Leave for twenty minutes to thicken. Stir before serving.

Joe's faked ecstatic beans

Joe is Evie's spiritual father – they have a very special bond. He loves to mess about in the kitchen, and out of all his creations Faked Beans **is definitely the best. For this book I've adapted it to make it more nutritious and too ecstatic for our own good.**

Soak the pine nuts, goji berries and sundried tomatoes in water for at least twenty minutes, then drain and rinse. Stone the dates.

Blend everything apart from the pine nuts in a high-speed blender.

Pour the sauce over the pine nuts, mix and serve as is, or put in a dehydrator for half an hour or so at 115°F/46°C to enjoy warm. If you're in a hurry, you can warm it gently in a pan on a low flame, stirring all the time and testing with your finger until it becomes hand hot.

100g soaked pine nuts
50ml olive oil
50g goji berries
½ red pepper
4 sundried tomatoes
2 dates
¼ teaspoon paprika

Kerfuddled 'eggs' in tomato boats

2 medium plum tomatoes
4 green olives, stoned
20g avocado
Pinch of thyme
Pinch of turmeric

OK, there's not actually any eggs in here, but it kind of looks like there is. Serves two. Keep for one day when refrigerated in a sealed container.

Cut the tomatoes in half. Scoop out and discard the insides.

Finely chop the olives and avocado together in a bowl with the thyme and turmeric. Roughly mash these ingredients together with a fork. Spoon this mix into the tomatoes and serve.

Rascherry dip with fruit

Serves four. Keeps for four days when refrigerated in a sealed container.

50g raspberries
50g cherries
20g goji berries
30ml raw agave nectar
5ml fresh lime juice
Fruit of choice for dipping: pears and apples are great

Blend everything apart from the dipping fruit until smooth. If your little one likes it really smooth, pass through a sieve to discard the raspberry seeds. Then pour into a small bowl.

Quarter the fruit and serve on a plate with the dip.

solstice morning sunshine sparkles

I asked my Space Mum Ruth if she wanted to contribute a recipe, so she wrote a story for me to make up a recipe for! Here's Evie's Space Grandma Ruth:

Evie Popple's solstice sunrise magick morning

Evie Popple's bird friends called her from sleep early on solstice morning. Evie Popple was up and dressed in rainbow colours before she nudged Mummy Popple out of her sweet dreams. Evie Popple's night angels had already spun the most orgasmic live food breakfast and had it all packed with purple ribbons in Evie's most favourite bag.

Mummy Popple sat with her precious girl in her earth lap and they felt the love and magick of the tender moments before sunrise. The stillness healing the core of their being – and then as goddess beckoned, the sun lazily peeked beyond the horizon bringing a blush of colour and magick to the early morning sky. Clouds deepened their morning experience into red and pink and shades of crimson hue.

Evie Popple's eyes were nourished and open wide, and Mummy Popple felt the love in her heart so full that it might spill out all over her baby as they sat and were touched and stroked in love at the new day. The vibrant doing energy rested in adulatory stillness as the days energy blossomed into expression. A sunrise shared is love in action.

The magick of stillness scattered in minutes into 'Evie Popple action' as the sun tickled her tummy hunger. The two sat under the early morning sun rays and shared their alive breakfast.

250g hazelnuts
250g pecans
250g sunflower seeds
50g Salba or chia
50g sesame seeds
100g raisins or currants
50g dried banana
50g dried papaya or other tropical fruit
50ml raw agave nectar

These are great with nut mylk poured over them in a bowl, and are also good for dipping into when you're a little bit peckish. Vary this every time with different types of nuts, seeds and dried fruits. Serves about thirty portions. Keeps for about two months in a sealed container.

Soak all the seeds and nuts in water overnight. Rinse and drain them and leave for a further 12 hours. Rinse and drain the seeds and nuts again and add everything to a food processor. If you don't have a large food processor, you'll have to do this in two batches. Process all the ingredients with the S blade until it becomes a coarse meal. Turn it out onto lined dehydrator trays and dehydrate at 115°F/46°C for about six to eight hours, or until totally dry. Leave to cool before storing in a sealed container.

soups

You can eat soups as part of a larger meal, but they are also a meal in their own right. My soups always have extra bits in them and they become souperfoods in no time.

I'm surprised that Evie loves soups so much, and I'm also ecstatic about it. You can get so many nutrients into soups and because they're blended they're really easy to digest.

Our soups are usually warm. As long as you don't go over 115°F/46°C, your food won't cook and all the nutrients will remain intact. I add a little heat using warm water or by running the blender for a long time. You can also stir them very gently in a pan until as warm as a finger likes. Our soups are a welcome addition to our raw diet, especially on a UK winter evening.

Brian Can Soup

400ml water not quite boiled from a kettle
100g tomatoes
40g shelled hemp seeds
30g celery
20ml olive oil
10g red onion
1 teaspoon fresh lemon juice
½ teaspoon lemon peel
2 sprigs of parsley
10 basil leaves
½ clove of garlic
Pinch of Himalayan pink salt

Optional garnish
20g alfalfa sprouts
20g chopped tomatoes
10ml Udo's Choice oil
Pinch of Seagreens

This is like that canned tomato soup that I used to eat when I was called Sharon and watched Playaway. Brian Cant was my hero and my mum even got me his signed photo. Serves two. Keeps for two days when refrigerated in a sealed container.

Put everything into a high-speed blender and blend until smooth and creamy. Garnish if you want, and serve immediately.

Monster Slime

500ml fresh coconut water
20g young coconut jelly (optional)
½ avocado
5g spirulina powder
½ teaspoon of lemon peel

This is a bright green cold meal that makes children inquisitive and excited about what they're about to encounter. It's very filling so the portions aren't big. Serves two. Keeps for two days when refrigerated in a sealed container.

Stone and skin the avocado. Add everything to a high-speed blender and blend until smooth and creamy. Serve with flax crackers or salad.

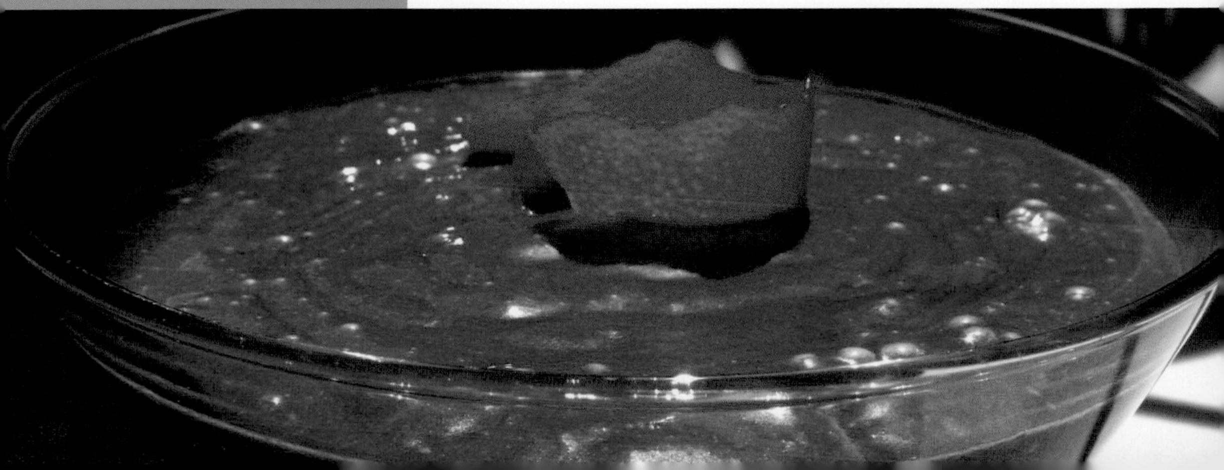

This is a lovely warm and filling soup. Serves two. Keeps for two days when refrigerated in a sealed container.

Stone and skin the avocado. Put all the ingredients into your high-powered blender and blend until smooth. Serve in two lovely big bowls, drizzle with extra oil, and sprinkle a few more Seagreens on top before tucking right in.

400ml water not quite boiled from a kettle
70g shelled hempseeds
½ cucumber
½ avocado
½ red pepper
1 small tomato
1 celery stalk
1 clove of garlic
¼ small red onion
10ml Udo's Choice oil

Optional garnish
10ml hemp seed oil
5g Seagreens or powdered broccoli sprouts

Leek and sweet potato soup

You wouldn't know this was raw because the blender shatters all the cell walls of the potato and makes it very creamy indeed. Serves two. Keeps for two days when refrigerated in a sealed container.

Blend all ingredients in a high-speed blender until very creamy, then serve.

100ml water not quite boiled from a kettle
50g leek, outer leaves removed
120g sweet potato
20g raw tahini
5g fresh dill

Right said med

- 110g celery
- 100g baby tomatoes
- 30g sundried tomatoes
- 20ml olive oil
- 2g fresh chives
- 2g fresh rosemary
- ¼ clove of garlic
- Pinch of Himalayan pink salt

Too sexy for a soup, it will triple up as a dip and salad dressing. Serves two. Keeps for two days when refrigerated in a sealed container.

Soak the sundried tomatoes in water for at least an hour. Blend everything in a high-speed blender, keeping some texture.

Red gazpacho soup

- 12 medium tomatoes
- ½ apple
- 5g fresh chives
- 8 basil leaves
- ½ cup cold water
- Ice to serve

Served cold over ice in the summer, it may stop your little one from melting like a crayon left in the conservatory. Serves two. Keeps for two days when refrigerated in a sealed container.

Core and peel the apple. In a high-speed blender, blend the water, apple, and two-thirds of the tomatoes and pepper until smooth. Finely chop the remaining food ingredients and mix into the liquid. Serve in bowls over ice.

Green gazpacho soup

110g celery
150g courgettes
30g pine nuts
1 medium avocado
½ clove of garlic
5g parsley
5g coriander
Pinch of unrefined sea salt

Optional garnish
10g pine nuts
Pinch of parsley
10g alfalfa sprouts

Serve cold over ice to bring arctic refreshment to a summer's day. Serves two. Keeps for two days when refrigerated in a sealed container.

Soak the pine nuts in water for at least an hour, drain and rinse. Blend all the soup ingredients until smooth. Serve over ice and top with the garnish if required.

Mild creamy butternut curried soup

300g butternut squash
80ml water not quite boiled from a kettle
80g raw coconut chips
40g red onion
20g fresh coriander
2 teaspoons mild curry powder
Pinch of Himalayan pink salt

Just like the sweet potato soup, this has an extremely creamy texture as the blender shatters the cell walls of the squash. Serves two. Keeps for two days when refrigerated in a sealed container.

Blend everything in a high-speed blender until very creamy. Serve immediately.

Give peas a chance

220g courgette
120g petit pois
60g lambs lettuce
6 mint leaves
Pinch of Himalayan pink salt

I've never understood Evie's love of peas, so she has this soup without me while singing her favourite song. "All we are saying is give peas a chance." Serves two. Keeps for two days when refrigerated in a sealed container.

Blend everything in a high-speed processor until creamy. Serve immediately while watching John Lennon on YouTube.

Spinach and parsley soup

200g spinach
2 medium avocados
10g parsley
¼ teaspoon barleygrass powder
Pinch of Himalayan pink salt

We love anything with parsley in. I think Evie was actually Parsley the Lion from The Herb Garden in a previous life. Well, she is a Leo. Serves two. Keeps for one day when refrigerated in a sealed container.

Skin and stone the avocados. Blend everything in a high-speed blender until warm and creamy.

Spinach is very mild in taste and is very dense in nutrients. However, it contains oxalic acid which inhibits iron uptake, so we only eat it occasionally.

ragus and celery soup

l water not quite boiled
om a kettle
g avocado
g raw macadamia nuts
g celery
0g asparagus
50g golden flax seeds
30g basil
10g basil
1 teaspoon raw apple cider
vinegar
1 sundried tomato
10g white miso
5ml Udo's Choice oil

It's hard to make raw asparagus taste right for a child, but this soup just about does it. I love to add some onion relish to mine, but for some reason Evie refrains. Serves two. Keeps for two days when refrigerated in a sealed container.

Dice half of the avocado and place in the bottom of the soup bowls. Add all the other ingredients to your high-powered blender and blend until really smooth and creamy.

Top this with a few large basil leaves and some chopped asparagus tips if you have them. Serve immediately.

carrot and coriander soup

1 medium carrot
1 yellow pepper
¼ apple
¼ red onion
5g coriander
5ml Udo's Choice oil
Pinch of Himalayan pink salt

A classic flavour that everyone loves. Serves two. Keeps for two days when refrigerated in a sealed container.

Remove the seeds and stalk from the pepper. Put all the ingredients into a high-speed blender and blend until warm and smooth.

Salba mant

Everything I make with Salba turns to gold, it's dream. I lie in my bed going "Salba, Salba, Salba." Evi amounts of tamari all over her soup, and I enrich mine and pink salt. Serves two. Keeps for two days when refriger sealed container.

Soak the sea salad in water for ten minutes, and drain. Empty th Seagreens out of their capsules into a high-speed blender. Put all the ingredients except the sprouts and a fifth of the sea salad into the blender and blend until really smooth. Pour the soup into two bowls and top with the remaining sea salad and the sprouts.

Aspa

10

2 Sea

2g drie

500m

fr

14

5

Tigger's Vegetable soup

A spring taste without spring ingredients, which is very bouncy trouncy flouncy indeed. Serves two. Keeps for two days when refrigerated in a sealed container.

- 500ml hot water (from a kettle, but not quite boiled)
- 4 cauliflower florets
- 2 small leeks
- 12 baby sweetcorn
- 4 pak choi leaves
- 20ml olive oil
- 20ml raw agave nectar
- 5ml raw apple cider vinegar
- 10g white miso
- 10g barley miso

Finely chop the vegetables and marinate in all the other ingredients apart from the miso and water for about five minutes. Mix the miso with a little of the warm water to form a paste then add the rest of the water. Pour the miso stock over the marinated vegetables and serve while still warm.

Steiner Soup

Rudolph Steiner was one of the biggest peniyummies ever (a male heart-led genius). He invented Steiner schools and Waldorf salad*. I mixed it all up here to make Steiner soup. Serves two. Keeps for two days when refrigerated in a sealed container.

- 500ml hot water (from a kettle, but not quite boiled)
- 60g walnuts
- 4 broccoli florets
- ½ sweet pear
- 30g raw almond butter
- 20ml raw agave nectar
- 10g barley miso
- 10ml olive oil
- 5ml raw apple cider vinegar

Cut the broccoli and pear into child-friendly chunks and mix with the vinegar, agave nectar and olive oil. Allow this to marinate for about five minutes.

Blend half the walnuts with all of the almond butter, miso and hot water in a high-speed blender until totally smooth. Then pour over the broccoli and pear, and stir in the remaining walnuts. Serve while still warm.

*Not really.

cabbage and apple soup

500ml hot water (from a kettle, but not quite boiled)
100g cabbage
40g almond butter
20ml raw agave nectar
20ml olive oil
10g barley miso
1 apple
5ml apple cider vinegar
½ teaspoon dill seed
½ teaspoon fresh thyme

This is soothing and hearty at the same time. Serves two. Keeps for two days when refrigerated in a sealed container.

Finely shred the cabbage and chop the apple into small thin slices. Pour over the vinegar, agave nectar and olive oil, and sprinkle the herbs. Stir and leave to marinate for about five minutes.

Blend the miso, almond butter and hot water until totally smooth then pour over the rest of the ingredients to serve.

Coconuts are the breasts of mother earth. Look at the shape of them, and look at the life-giving water that flows from them. They even contain lauric acid, only available in milk. Lauric acid is antimicrobial, and that's why we eat coconut products every day.

Thai coconut soup

500ml coconut water
Jelly of one young coconut
¼ carrot
20g cabbage
5g galangal or ginger
5g lemongrass
5g raw coconut butter
1 kafir lime leaf
½ teaspoon lime zest
¼ teaspoon paprika
½ clove of garlic
Pinch of unrefined sea salt

Though it's highly flavoured, small ones love the creamy coconuttiness of this soup. Serves two. Keeps for two days when refrigerated in a sealed container.

Cut half of the coconut jelly or meat into ribbons and put to one side along with half the cabbage.

Blend all the other ingredients in a high-speed blender. When smooth and warm pour into bowls and add the coconut ribbons and finely sliced remaining cabbage.

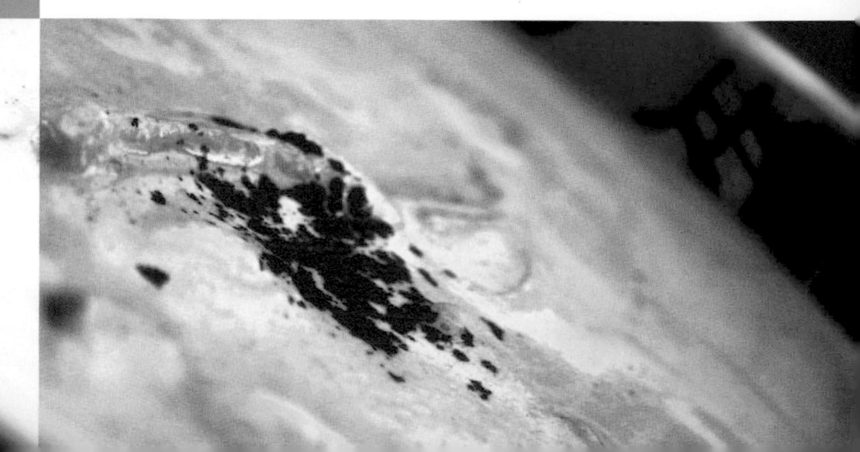

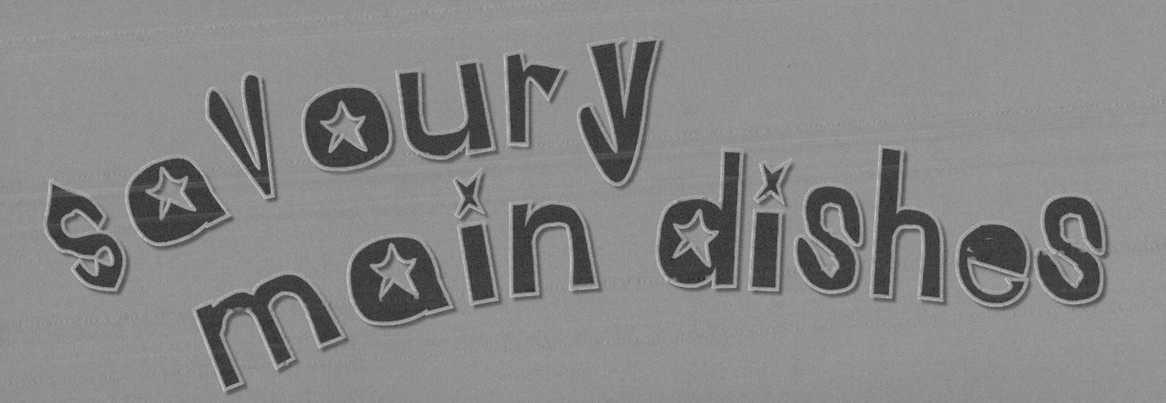

savoury main dishes

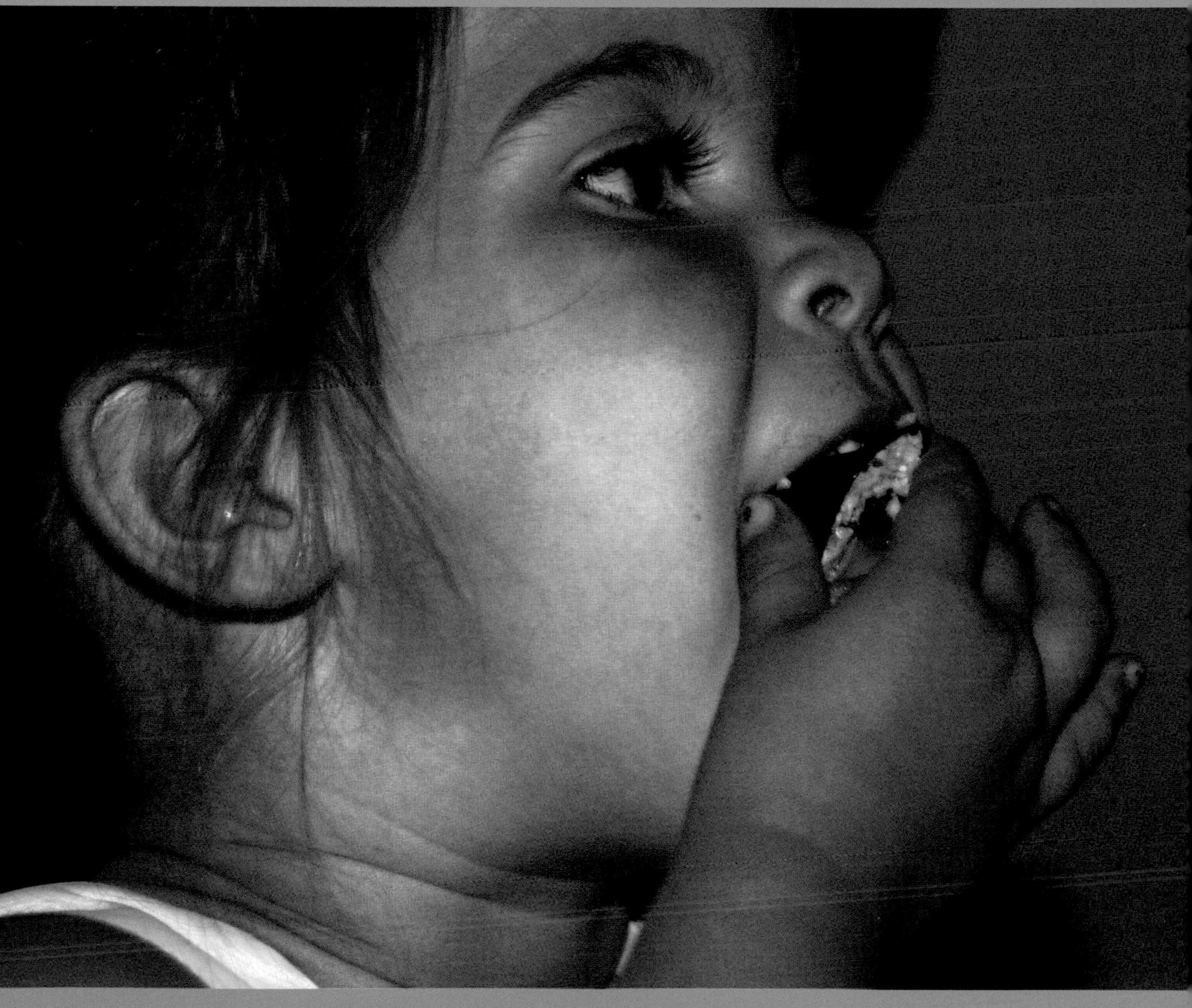

Large meals can intimidate small children, so it's best not to give them too much all at once. Remember that their stomach is the size of their fist. They should be eating several small meals and snacks, all made up of nutrient-dense food. They shouldn't be eating large bowlfuls of nutrient-deficient pasta and rice "for energy".

Introduce main meals with love and care. I started Evie eating meals by putting her on my knee so she could choose from my plate. Next to my breasts and beating heart, she felt comfortable in her experiments and she had no pressure from me about having to leave an empty plate.

Deep down goji loaf

200g pumpkin seeds
100g shelled hemp seeds
50g golden flax seeds
50g goji berries
20g green olives
20g fresh parsley
20g fresh basil
1 red onion
1 celery stalk
2 red, orange or yellow peppers
10g dark unpasteurised miso

The herbs and miso give this recipe an incredibly intense flavour. It shows how great goji berries are in savoury foods. They come from the nightshade family, so they substitute tomatoes really well. Serves about ten. Keeps for five days when refrigerated in a sealed container.

Grind the pumpkin seeds, hemp seeds and flax seeds to a rough flour. Pour this into a large mixing bowl.

Soak the goji berries in water for at least two minutes, then drain. Skin the onion and deseed and stalk the peppers. Add these to a high-speed blender or food processor. Add the olives, goji berries, celery, miso and herbs. Blend this mixture until it resembles the consistency of salsa. Pour this into the mixing bowl and mix all ingredients together to form a soft dough.

Turn this out onto a lined dehydrator sheet and form a loaf shape. Dehydrate at 115°F/46°C for 24 hours or until it's set in the middle. You can also form a few little patties before making the loaf, as they make great snacks while you're waiting for the big one to be ready.

creamy mushroom and sweetcorn pie

You wouldn't know this was raw. It's tender, warm and creamy, all the attributes that children love in food. It's quite faffy to make so save it for a special occasion. Serves two small portions, but it's very filling. Keeps for two days in a sealed container in the fridge.

2 large flat field mushrooms
150ml water
100g raw pine nuts
50g sweetcorn cut from the cob
50g wild mushrooms
50g cucumber
½ celery stalk
5ml tamari
5ml raw agave nectar
Juice of ½ lemon
¼ teaspoon ground cumin
¼ teaspoon fresh thyme
Pinch of nutmeg
Pinch of Himalayan pink salt

Mix the tamari, salt, lemon juice and water in a large bowl.

Remove the stalk from the large mushrooms. Put them in the mixture (gill side up) and ensure the gills are all covered in water. Add more water if needed. If you have shiitake as your wild mushrooms, remove the stalks and thinly slice them. If you have oyster mushrooms, leave them whole or break them into large pieces. For other wild mushrooms, slice and dice them according to thickness. Add all the mushrooms to the soaking water. Feel free to set some aside for decoration. Add the sweetcorn to the water. Ensure everything is covered in the water. Leave this to soak for at least one hour, and preferably overnight.

When your mushrooms and sweetcorn have marinated, drain them from the water, reserving the water. Place the large mushrooms on a plate each.

Remove the skin from the cucumber. In a high-speed blender, blend the remaining unused ingredients until you have a smooth white sauce. Mix this white sauce in with the wild mushrooms and sweetcorn. Pile this mixture onto the large mushrooms. Place plates into your dehydrator. Dehydrate at 115°F/46°C for one to four hours. It will taste increasingly tender the longer you leave it.

Tip: Make mushroom gravy with the leftover marinade by blending it with two soaked sundried tomatoes and a teaspoon of flax powder.

Sweet fragrant Veg in da mix

50g okra
4 chestnut mushrooms
½ courgette
3 cherry tomatoes
½ red onion
2 spring onions
10ml yacon syrup
4 kafir lime leaves
10ml hemp sauce
5g coriander

A light meal, this is revered by raw kiddies throughout the universe. The universe loves you and wants you to eat raw food. Serves two. Keeps for three days when refrigerated in a sealed container.

Slice, chop and cut the vegetables into small chunks. Place them all into a large glass dish with the syrup, sauce, leaves and most of the coriander. Save a little coriander to season with.

Place the dish in your dehydrator and dehydrate at 115°F/46°C for two to four hours. You may wish to stir this halfway through. The courgettes should be soft. Before serving, fish out the lime leaves and throw them in the compost.

100g mushrooms
20g Enjevita
20g hemp oil
50g peas
50g sweetcorn
10g soya lecithin
5g tamari
5g Seagreens

Always remembering the Rainbow Warrior, and saluting those who love our planet in ginormous ways. Serves two. Keeps for two days in a sealed container in the fridge.

Thinly slice the mushrooms, put them in a bowl and pour on the oil and tamari. Mix thoroughly.

Add all the other ingredients and mix thoroughly again.

Serve immediately or marinate for a couple of hours to soften the mushrooms further.

okra casserole

Serve with raw bread for a filling meal or with a green salad for something lighter. This dish is high in silica which helps bones become nice and strong and makes your skin shine beautifully. Serves four. Keeps for three days when refrigerated in a sealed container.

- 200g cucumber
- 200g tomatoes
- 175g okra
- 50g goji berries, soaked in water for 2 minutes
- 50g sesame seeds
- 20g coriander
- 10g broccoli
- 10g golden flax seeds
- 1 small clove of garlic
- 1 courgette
- 1 yellow pepper
- 1 celery stalk
- Seeds from 2 cardamom pods
- 5 fresh rosemary leaves
- ¼ teaspoon ground nutmeg

Top and tail the okra, then finely slice it into a large flat-bottomed bowl. Mince the garlic. Top and tail the courgette and grate it. Deseed and finely dice the pepper. Add all these ingredients to the bowl along with the sesame seeds.

In a high-speed blender or food processor, blend the rest of the ingredients until smooth. Add this sauce to the bowl and mix everything well. Put into a dehydrator with the bowl on a tray. Dehydrate at 115°F/46°C for four to six hours, mixing a few times.

Some nights I think it's great for Evie to have a choice of lots of different foods. It's like a tray picnic in our lounge. We put lots of different foods on a tray and we dip, munch, crunch and cuddle. It's lovely. Here's a selection of what we use, but it all depends on the wonders held by my cupboards at the time. I like to include at least one fatty food, one veggie food and one sweet food.

- Guacamole
- Sticks of celery, cucumber, carrots, okra and baby sweetcorn
- Apple slices
- Seeds soaked in tamari and dehydrated
- Goji berries
- Olives
- Alfalfa, sunflower and radish sprouts
- Gherkins
- Flax crackers
- Raw chocolates
- Raisins

Arrange everything in a beautiful way, because presentation is everything, and serve.

vegetable maki

SAF rice, shiitake, shiso, sweet pepper and wasabi aioli

No, I haven't gone all gourmet on you. Überchef Chad Sarno contributed this beautiful recipe especially for Evie. She went to SAF one night and devoured this then went all shy on Chad when he asked her if she would like it in her book. OK, she didn't eat the wasabi, that's the bit for grown ups. I haven't converted Chad's measurements to metric, so dig out your spoons and cups and enjoy this perfect creation. (OK, 1T=14ml.) Thank you, Chad, for being the best chef in the Universe! Recipe and photo is © www.rawchef.com.

vegetable sushi maki roll

Vegetable Sushi Maki Roll
- 1 nori sheet
- 2 ounces parsnip or cauliflower rice (see recipe below)
- Red peppers julienne
- Shiso leaf
- Shiitake sliced thin and marinated (equal parts shoyu and olive oil)
- Wasabi aioli (see recipe below)

On a nori sheet spread ⅓ cup parsnip/cauliflower rice evenly — be sure to leave a bit of space on top and bottom for rolling, continue to assemble with assorted vegetables stacking in center, tuck and roll.

Slice into seven pieces and serve with wasabi and shoyu.

Parsnip (or cauliflower), Sesame White Rice

Parsnip (or cauliflower), Sesame White Rice
Makes seven cups
- 6 C cauliflower florets or peeled parsnip
- 1.5 C pine nuts
- 3 T flax oil
- 1 T toasted sesame oil (we use raw but it doesn't taste the same)
- 1 T mirin, rice vinegar, or apple cider vinegar
- 1 T course sea salt
- 3 T green onion or chives minced
- 2 T black sesame seeds

In a food processor, pulse all ingredients until finely minced (white rice consistency).

Use this as a base and add multiple variations. Serve with sushi maki or as a side for salads.

wasabi Aioli

Wasabi Aioli
- 2 C cashews soaked 10-12 hours
- ¼ C olive oil
- 1 T apple cider vinegar
- 1 T agave nectar
- 2 cloves garlic
- ¼ inch piece of ginger root
- 3 T green onion
- 2½ T wasabi powder or ¼ fresh wasabi root finely shredded
- 1 T Sea salt

In a high-speed blender, blend all ingredients until smooth. You may need to add water to get desired consistency.

Hemp croquettes

200g carrot pulp
100g shelled hemp seeds
100g raw almonds
1 red pepper
1 clove of garlic
2 sundried tomatoes, soaked for at least a few minutes
1 teaspoon dried mixed herbs
1 level teaspoon paprika (mild)
Pinch of sea salt
Extra shelled hemp seeds for rolling in (the croquettes, not you, you'll get covered!)

Lovely and light, your small one will delight in rolling these around the plate. She might even eat them. I make these straight after making a juice, so that I've got fresh carrot pulp and I don't need to clean the juicer twice. Makes about 12-18 depending on size. Keeps for five days when refrigerated in a sealed container.

Blend everything apart from the pulp in a food processor until well mixed. Add it to a large bowl and add the carrot pulp. Mix everything together by hand to get some extra love into it.

Take a lump of mixture about the size of a golfball, roll it into a ball, then a sausage, and then flatten the ends by standing them briefly on a plate. This mixture is very soft, so it's easy to work with.

Roll each croquette into some spare seeds so they stick to the whole croquette. Place them on a dehydrator tray then dehydrate at 115°F/46°C for about six to eight hours. This is great timing if you do it in the morning, as it makes them ready for a lovely warm teatime!

Pesto stuffed tomatoes

I'm surprised that toddlers like this, but they do. All those herbs are really nutritious too. Goes well with a light salad and olives. Serves three. Keeps for three days when refrigerated in a sealed container.

Cut the tomatoes in half and scoop out the seeds, keeping them in a cup. Blend all the other ingredients except the oil with a hand blender (there's not enough to use a high-speed blender).

Add a dessertspoon of the tomato juice from the discarded seeds and the oil, and stir it all together (don't blend the oil).

Stuff the tomatoes with the mixture and dehydrate for about an hour at 115°F/46°C. Serve.

100g pine nuts
6 medium tomatoes
30g basil
20g parsley
10 stalks of chives
2 sprigs of oregano
10ml olive oil
¼ clove of garlic
Pinch of Himalayan pink salt

Nessie swims in her lake

200g shelled hemp seeds
50g raw tahini
20g dried wakame
1 courgette
2 sundried tomatoes
10ml raw hemp oil
½ red pepper
Juice of ¼ lemon
2 sprigs of fresh coriander
1 clove of garlic (optional)
1 level teaspoon kelp powder

When I was about nine years old my Auntie Shirley and Uncle Ray took us to Scotland in their caravan. We drove to Loch Ness and I saw the Monster! Of course nobody believed me because we'd driven past it before they could see where I was pointing to. I cried my heart out as they laughed at me. I'd never seen an image of the monster but when we got back to the caravan Shirley showed me a book she had with three pictures that were allegedly her (Nessie, not Shirley). One of them was identical to what I'd seen. I was suddenly overjoyed and no longer cared that everyone laughed at me. This melt-in-your-mouth-and-ask-for-more recipe is a thank you to Nessie for showing me her magic. Serves two. Keeps for two days in a sealed container in the fridge.

Soak the wakame and sundried tomatoes for one to four hours. Remove the seeds and stalk from the pepper. Blend all the ingredients except the courgette and wakame in a high-speed blender until smooth and creamy.

Cut the wakame into bite-sized pieces because small ones can't chew it very well. Grate the courgette and mix with the wakame.

Pour the dressing on top and mix everything together. See how Nessie (the wakame) winds her way through the lake (the dressing). Serve with celery and carrot sticks if desired.

Sage and onion sosages

These sosages are really easy to shape, and they taste so lovely that your child may not actually get to try one! Makes about twelve large sosages. Keeps for about seven days when refrigerated in a sealed container.

200g raw pumpkin seeds
200g raw sunflower seeds
100g brazil nuts
20g golden flax seeds
1 small red onion
1 apple
5 dried apricots
1 red pepper
1 sundried tomato
5g fresh thyme
5g paprika
10 fresh sage leaves
1 clove of garlic
½ teaspoon kelp powder
Pinch of Himalayan pink salt

Sprout the pumpkin and sunflower seeds by soaking overnight. Drain, rinse and leave for another twelve hours. Rinse again, then leave overnight. Rinse the next morning and start the recipe.

Soak the sundried tomato in water for at least an hour, then drain and rinse. Finely chop the sundried tomato, garlic, apricots and sage.

Grind the flax seeds to a flour. Core the apple. Remove seeds and stalk from the pepper. Put all the ingredients into a high-speed blender and blend until the mixture sticks together — but don't turn it into a paté.

Make sosage shapes with the mixture and place the sosages on a dehydrator tray. Dehydrate at 115°F/46°C for eight hours, or until they're not sticky in the middle.

Stir crazy

100g carrot
80g okra
60g fresh shiitake mushrooms
50g leeks
10ml tamari
10ml raw agave nectar
10ml olive oil
5g ginger root
½ clove of garlic
Juice of ½ lemon

Evie's favourite evening meals are ones like this. Full of taste, warm, and juicy — just like her mummy's booboos. Serves four. Keeps for two days in a sealed container in the fridge.

Julienne all the vegetables and thinly slice the mushrooms. Finely chop the ginger and garlic. Mix all ingredients together.

Marinate in a fridge for 24 hours (optional) then bring to room temperature and eat or place in a dehydrator at 115°F/46°C for four to eight hours. If possible, stir half way through.

Deep Sea patties

3 carrots
3 celery stalks
1 red onion
300g raw almonds
20g Seagreens
20g Clearspring sea salad
5g kelp powder
5g golden flax seed, ground
4 sundried tomatoes, soaked at least one hour
10g chives
Pinch of Himalayan pink salt

These make good lunch bag snacks as well as main meal additions. They're slightly crunchy with a really deep-sea taste. Makes about 20 patties. Keeps for seven days in a sealed container in the fridge.

Blend all the ingredients except the chives in a food processor until they're at the kibbled stage. Transfer one third of the mixture to a high-speed blender and blend until fully homogenised.

Chop the chives with scissors into 5mm pieces straight into a big mixing bowl. Put both mixtures into the mixing bowl and mix everything together by hand.

Form the patties by hand and place them on a dehydrator tray. Dehydrate at 115°F/46°C for six to eight hours before serving.

Tagliatelle devoted to you

Full of minerals and great-tasting, sea spaghetti is a strange yet well-appreciated creature in our house. Everybody who's introduced to it loves it, so it's a great one to serve to non-raw people. The sauce calms down the overexcited seaweed to make a mellow meal fit for a tiny god or goddess. Serves two. Keeps for two days in a sealed container in the fridge.

- 100g sea spaghetti
- 100g pine nuts
- 1 yellow pepper
- 1 clove of garlic
- 75ml water
- 1 spring onion, chopped
- 5g maca powder
- Pinch of paprika
- Parsley to garnish

Soak the sea spaghetti for twenty minutes in warm but not hot water.

Meanwhile, core and seed the pepper. Blend the pine nuts with the pepper, garlic, spring onion, maca and water until very creamy.

Rinse the sea spaghetti and discard the water (or use it in another recipe as it contains lots of flavour and goodness). Put equal amounts of sea spaghetti on two plates, make a well and pour over the cream. Dress with a few extra pine nuts, the paprika and some parsley. Serve and devour with love.

strawberry and hemp burritos

100g shelled hemp seeds
50g raw cashew nuts
1 avocado
½ red pepper
4 strawberries
5g hemp leaf powder
½ teaspoon Crystal Manna
5ml hemp oil
4 large romaine lettuce leaves or cabbage leaves
Pinch of Himalayan salt

This is nice and sweet, yet really grounding. How many children get to eat strawberries for their main meal? Serves two to four depending on age. Keeps for two days in a sealed container in the fridge when not assembled into the leaves.

Blend all the ingredients except the strawberries and leaves until smooth. Pour even amounts of the mixture into the centre of the leaves. Thinly slice the strawberries and arrange on top.

Roll the back and the sides into the centre, making a burrito shape. Eat from the front, where it's still open.

comforting vegetable casserole

250ml hot water
1 avocado
20g golden flax seeds
20g cauliflower
20g sprouted seeds, such as alfalfa
10g spinach or watercress
5g Seagreens
5g green powdered superfood
5g raw hemp seed butter
2 sundried tomatoes

Soak the sundried tomatoes in water for one to two hours then drain. Grind the flax seeds to a flour. Peel, stone and mash the avocado with the flax and Seagreens in two pudding bowls.

Cut the cauliflower into small pieces. Chop the spinach or watercress. Dice the sundried tomatoes. Add these along with the green superfood and the sprouts to the bowls. Mix it up to coat the vegetables.

Pour hot water into the bowl and mix until you get a good casserole consistency. Serve warm immediately.

Russell Brand's hair fell on my plate

If I am not destined to be Russell's soulmate, then all I can do is invent a dish that looks like his hair. One year we made a Russell fairy to top our minimalist Christmas tree. Evie loves Russell and wants him to be her step-father (that's my affirmation; she doesn't understand the word step-father yet). Serves two. Keeps for two days in a sealed container in the fridge.

- 100g dried sea spaghetti
- 50g sunflower sprouts
- 10ml Udo's Choice oil
- 50g raw tahini
- 50g white miso
- ½ teaspoon Blue Manna
- ½ teaspoon lion's mane mushroom powder

Soak the sea spaghetti in warm water for at least thirty minutes, drain and rinse. Add to a large mixing bowl.

Remove any shells from the sunflower sprouts and add to the bowl.

In a small bowl, mix the miso, tahini, Blue Manna, lion's mane and oil. Pour into the large mixing bowl and massage everything together with your hands before serving.

Golden nuggets

220g pumpkin seeds
260g sunflower seeds
50g golden flax seeds, finely ground
10g Seagreens
1 small red onion
1 apple
5 dried apricots
1 red pepper
1 sundried tomato
5g fresh parsley
5g paprika
1 clove of garlic
½ teaspoon finely ground black pepper
Pinch of Himalayan sea salt

You can make these into little nuggets or larger cutlets, depending on the preferences of your child or the occasion. Makes about twelve cutlets or about thirty nuggets. Keeps for about seven days when refrigerated in a sealed container.

Soak the sundried tomatoes in water for at least an hour, then drain and rinse. Remove the seeds and stalk from the pepper. Core the apple. Finely chop the sundried tomato, garlic, apricots and parsley. Grind the flax seeds to a flour.

Add all the ingredients except half of the flax seeds and half of the paprika to a food processor and process until finely ground and sticky, but not a paté.

Mix the remaining flax and paprika together on a small plate.

Take one piece at a time and make cutlet or nugget shapes with them. Roll in the flax mixture and place them on a dehydrator tray. Dehydrate at 115°F/46°C for about six to eight hours.

crocodile's cauliflower crock

This is a kiddie's curry, very mild yet with a definite bite. Did you know one of the differences between an alligator and a crocodile is that you can't see an alligator's teeth when their mouth is closed? I'm sure you wouldn't want to see a crocodile when its mouth is open! Serves two. Keeps for two days in a sealed container in the fridge.

200g cauliflower
150ml water
100g raw peanuts
60g tomatoes
30g currants or raisins
20g fresh basil
½ red pepper
20ml raw pumpkin oil
8 sundried tomatoes
5g medium curry powder
5g paprika
½ clove of garlic
½ inch of ginger
Juice of ½ lemon
4 sprigs parsley
Pinch of Himalayan pink salt

Soak the sundried tomatoes in water for at least twenty minutes, then drain and rinse.

Meanwhile cut the cauliflower florets away from the stalk and discard the stalk. Cut the florets into little bite-sized pieces.

Blend all ingredients except the cauliflower in a high-speed blender or hand blender to make a sauce.

Put everything into a shallow wide-bottomed dish and mix well. Put this dish into your dehydrator and dehydrate for two to four hours at 115°F/46°C before serving.

Barbapapa's got a face full

10 cabbage leaves
1 avocado
10g Enjevita
20ml hemp oil
20g raw sesame seeds
10ml raw apple cider vinegar
2 sundried tomatoes, soaked
Juice of ½ lemon
1 teaspoon caraway seeds
¼ teaspoon Himalayan pink salt

For some reason Evie adores cabbage. Here I stack it high on her special Barbapapa plate and sometimes we watch the original Barbapapas on YouTube while eating it because it's good to let a 21st century child think she's living in the 70s. Serves two. Keeps for two days in a sealed container in the fridge.

Soak the sundried tomatoes in water for at least twenty minutes, then drain and rinse.

Blend the salt, vinegar, caraway seeds, tomatoes, lemon juice and oil in a small blender.

Remove the large central veins from the cabbage and thinly slice the leaves. Toss all ingredients into a large bowl and leave to marinate for thirty minutes to two hours.

Spacado

Fresh and creamy, this dish is fun to suck up! Serves two with a side salad. Keeps for one day in a sealed container in the fridge.

Using a spirooli or spiraliser, create spaghetti out of the courgette. Thinly slice the olives. Skin and stone the avocado, then cut it into cubes. Mix up all the ingredients, and then serve.

1 courgette
1 avocado
50g green olives, stoned
20g raw vegan pesto
5g minced coriander leaf
½ teaspoon coriander seeds

cream of asparagus pies

Not our everyday fayre, we make these when someone special is popping over. That'll be us, then. You'll need four of those pretty deep-fill little pie moulds for this. Serves four with a side salad. Keeps for three days in a sealed container in the fridge.

For the pastry
60g goji berries
60g shelled hemp seeds
60g golden flax seeds
20g raw mesquite powder
Pinch of Himalayan pink salt
(20g mesquite powder for rolling the pastry)

For the filling
100g asparagus (hard ends discarded). Reserve 4 tips for decoration
100g raw macadamia nuts
30g raw mesquite powder
20ml olive oil
1 spring onion
15g parsley
15g basil
10ml raw agave nectar
1 teaspoon lemon rind
5ml lemon juice
Pinch of Himalayan pink salt

Soak the goji berries in water for five minutes (discard the soak water afterwards). Grind the flax seeds using the dry jug of your high-speed blender. Add all the pastry ingredients to a food processor and blend until a dough forms. Remove from the food processor and divide into four equal pieces. Roll each piece in some extra mesquite powder and press into the moulds.

Blend all the filling ingredients in a high-speed blender. A hand-held blender may work OK but raw asparagus can be tough to break down, and the aim is to create a creamy puree. Pour equal amounts of this mixture into your pie shells and top with an asparagus tip.

Dehydrate for two hours, then gently prise them out of their cases and dehydrate for a further six hours before serving or refrigerating.

sprouted quinoa tabouleh

80g quinoa
30g spinach leaves
½ cucumber
1 carrot
10g parsley
Juice of ¼ lemon

This is easy to eat and filling. Serve with an outrageous sauce. Serves two with a side salad. Keeps for three days in a sealed container in the fridge.

Soak the quinoa in water overnight. Rinse, drain and sprout for a day. The next day, rinse the quinoa sprouts again and place on kitchen roll or a clean tea towel to absorb as much excess water as possible.

Grate the carrot, finely chop the parsley, dice the cucumber and toss all ingredients into a happy melange before serving.

Seed and mushroom loaf

Keep some of this mixture aside to use as a really nice paté. Serves about ten. Keeps for five days when refrigerated in a sealed container.

300g sunflower seeds
200g button or chestnut mushrooms
200g shelled hemp seeds
30g dried shiitake mushrooms
1 tomato
½ red pepper
4 sundried tomatoes
20ml olive oil
Juice of 1 lemon
10g Seagreens powder or kelp powder
20g fresh parsley
1 dessertspoon paprika
Pinch of unrefined sea salt

Soak the sunflower seeds and sundried tomatoes for at least an hour, then drain and rinse. Finely slice the fresh mushrooms and put them in a bowl with the shiitake mushrooms, oil, salt and lemon juice. Mix well and marinate for about four hours. Please don't skimp on this time or the loaf won't be so juicy.

Finely chop the parsley. Remove seeds and stalk from the pepper. Blend everything in a food processor, but don't liquidise it because it needs some texture.

Shape into a loaf about 3cm high (you can also make burger shapes). Dehydrate on a tray at 115°F/46°C for eight hours.

MushNuggets

4 large flat mushrooms
100g golden flax seeds
20ml olive oil
20ml water
1 teaspoon paprika
Pinch of Himalayan pink salt

These are lovely with a tomato dip. A great finger food, too. Serves four. Keeps for five days when refrigerated in a sealed container.

Grind the flax seeds into a fine flour. Slice the mushrooms about 3-4mm wide. Place them in a bowl and add the salt, water and olive oil. Mix together so the mushrooms are coated on all sides.

Mix the paprika, pepper and flax flour together. Toss the mushrooms in this mixture. Place the mushrooms on a dehydrator tray and dehydrate at 115°F/46°C for two hours before serving.

comforting miso casserole

Another quick and easy one to keep Starvin' Marvin at bay. For the hot water, I boil the kettle but stop it before it actually boils. Don't use hot tap water! Serves two. Keeps for two days in a sealed container in the fridge.

250ml hot water
1 avocado
20g golden flax seeds
2 chestnut mushrooms
20g sprouted seeds, such as alfalfa
10g dark barley miso
5g green powdered superfood

Grind the flax seeds to a flour. Mash the avocado with the flax and green superfood in two pudding bowls. Finely dice the mushrooms and add them to the bowls with the miso. Mix it all up to coat the mushrooms, then allow to marinate for a few minutes. Add the green superfood and the sprouts to this mix.

Pour hot water onto the bowls, and mix each one until you get a good casserole consistency.

Roastly Veg

- 100g mushrooms
- 2 courgettes
- 4 tomatoes
- 1 red pepper
- 1 yellow pepper
- 1 red onion (optional)
- 1 clove of garlic (optional, depending on child's age and taste)
- 20ml olive oil
- 10ml tamari or ½ teaspoon Himalayan salt in 10ml water

These vegetables look and taste as good as the roast version, but all the nutrients are still intact. It keeps well in the fridge or you can use leftovers to make tasty soups or even chutneys. Serves four. Keeps for three days in a sealed container in the fridge.

Slice and quarter the courgettes. Cut the tomatoes into eights. Slice the mushrooms. Thinly slice the peppers and onion. Mince the garlic.

Add all the ingredients to a wide-bottomed bowl and mix really well.

Dehydrate at 115°F/46°C for at least two hours. You can eat it at this stage, but it's best dehydrated for around eight hours. I always stir this a few times while it's in the dehydrator. The juices come out and help the process, so you really don't need much liquid to start it off.

salads

I can't imagine life without a salad a day. Or more. Salads can be as simple or as complex as you like; I hope this range inspires you to create your own. The best thing about making salads with children is that they eat it as it's being prepared. Oh how it fills my heart to have Evie atop my chopping board.

- 20g flatleaf parsley
- 10 olives, pitted
- 1 raw beetroot
- 10g Clearspring sea salad
- ½ avocado

A warming salad with lovely colours. There's a reason we see in colour — so we're magnetised to high-antioxidant food. Pat yourself on the back and make this at the same time because you're great at mothertasking. Serves one toddler and there's a little bit left over for mummy. Will keep for one day when refrigerated in a sealed container.

Soak the sea salad in water for ten minutes, then drain and rinse. Skin, stone and cube the avocado, grate the beetroot, shred the parsley and slice the olives. Add all ingredients to a plate and mix well.

Great curly carrots

You need a spiral slicer for this. If you don't have one you can grate the carrots, but then you have to cross out this title and call it Grate straight carrots. **Mummies love this with a big pile of spinach or watercress. Serves two as a side salad. Keeps for four days when refrigerated in a sealed container.**

5ml water
40g raw almond butter
20g fresh parsley
Juice of 1 orange
1 medium carrot
10ml raw agave nectar
5ml raw hemp oil
½ teaspoon cayenne powder
¼ teaspoon apple cider vinegar

If using a spiraliser, set it to the pasta setting. If using a spirooli, use the finest blade. Spiral slice the carrots and put them in a bowl.

Blend all the remaining ingredients until creamy. Pour this over the carrots.

Take a leek

This salad has the full gamut of flavours yet is simple to make and has no dressing. Serves two. Keeps for one day when refrigerated in a sealed container.

2 carrots
1 apple
1 small leek
60g raw pecan nuts
20g raw macadamia nuts

Grate the carrots, core and roughly chop the apple, finely slice and chop the leek and combine with nuts. Mix it up.

Kale on Sunday

20 stalks of dinosaur kale (cavelo nero) or curly kale
10 cherry tomatoes
50g shelled hemp seeds
30g raw pine nuts
40ml olive oil
50g Peruvian olives
30g fresh flat leaved parsley
10g raw coconut butter
5g purple corn extract

This salad is so dense that it fills every pocket of your child's existence. Eating good food takes up just enough time that you can't be tempted to read the papers, ensuring you never get drawn into Ye Olde 3D Worlde. Serves one grown up and one toddler but you might fight over it. Keeps for three days when refrigerated in a sealed container.

Shave the olives into a wide-bottomed bowl, discarding the stones. Cut the stalks out of the kale and use for juicing or in another recipe. Roll the kale up into a long, thin cigar. Slice through it at 1cm intervals. Add this to the bowl.

Quarter the tomatoes and finely chop the parsley, and add them to the bowl. Add the hemp seeds, pine nuts and purple corn extract. Add the olive oil and the coconut butter. Mix everything with your hands. Let your child join in. Massage the kale for five minutes with as much love as you can channel. Let it rest for an hour before serving. You can put this in the dehydrator for that hour, which will make it invitingly warm.

squish

Children are attracted to bright orange squash. They love to help make this one, and often eat handfuls of squash spaghetti as you make it. Serves four to six. Keeps for three days when refrigerated in a sealed container.

600g butternut squash (about one medium squash)
10g Seagreens
50ml raw hemp oil
100g raisins
Juice of 1 lime
¼ teaspoon Himalayan pink salt

Peel the squash and remove the seeds. Spiralise or grate the squash and add to a large casserole dish. Add all the other ingredients and then mix.

This is ready to eat as soon as you've made it, but it's much nicer if you marinate it overnight.

Filling Winter Salad

¼ white cabbage
¼ cauliflower
50g pecans
1 apple
1 pear
1 cucumber

Salads in the winter get chunkier and denser. Serves four as a side salad. Keeps for three days when refrigerated in a sealed container.

Finely shred the cabbage and place in a large bowl along with the pecans. Cut the florets of the cauliflower off the stalks so they are in small pieces and add those. Core and finely dice the apple, pear and cucumber so they are roughly the same size, add those to the bowl, mix everything and serve.

Ensalada Mexicana

This is very filling, pretty and sweet. I put this in a mould when I'm feeling too fancy. Serves four. Keeps for two days when refrigerated in a sealed container.

2 avocados
2 limes
½ plneapple
10g fresh coriander
40g celery
40g pumpkin seeds
1 teaspoon cumin
¼ red onion
1 tablespoon dried coriander

Peel and stone the avocados and roughly mash them. Cut the core from the pineapple and cube it. Finely chop the celery and onion. Roughly chop the fresh coriander.

Put all these ingredients into a bowl, squeeze one of the limes on top and add the remaining herbs and spices. Cut the remaining lime into quarters and place them in the centre of the dish to serve.

Princess Popple's Salad

8 baby corns
1 avocado
20g shelled hemp seeds
10g raw vegan pesto
4 leaves of romaine lettuce

This is one of Evie's favourite meals, and she always asks for seconds. She's getting in practice for when she has to kiss frogs. "Next." Serves two. Keeps for three days when refrigerated in a sealed container.

Cut the corn into little 5mm wheels. Peel, stone and dice the avocado. Shred the lettuce. Add everything to a bowl, mix and serve.

100g baby corn
20ml olive oil
10ml flax oil
10g raw hemp seed butter
½ teaspoon Seagreens
⅛ teaspoon Blue Manna
5g light unpasteurised miso

This kind of food transports us to paradise on earth. It's so super-nutritious that your child will grow before your very eyes. Maybe. Serves one small child who loves corn as a full salad meal. Keeps for two days when refrigerated in a sealed container.

Slice the corn into small wheels. Mix all the other ingredients together in a bowl, add the corn and coat it with the mixture.

There's something about celery slaw

Very clean and nibbly, this little salad goes well perched on a plate with other food. There's something about celery that I worship, and Evie's the same, but we don't keep any on our altar as it'd start to smell funny after a while. Serves four. Keeps for two days when refrigerated in a sealed container.

1 head of celery
1 avocado
Juice of ½ orange
40g raisins

Shred the celery using a mandolin or food processor with the slicing blade. Place this in a bowl and add the raisins. Blend the avocado and orange until smooth, and pour this over the celery. Mix well. Add some lovely fresh herbs if you like.

Ecstatically yours

50g quinoa
50g alfalfa sprouts
50g sunflower seeds
50g pumpkin seeds
2 courgettes
10g parsley
3 stalks celery
1 large tomato
20g goji berries

Salads can't help but make you ecstatic, and this one goes the extra mile with all these seeds and sprouts. Serves four. Keeps for two days when refrigerated in a sealed container.

Soak the quinoa in water overnight. Rinse, drain and sprout for a day. The next day, rinse the quinoa sprouts again and place on some kitchen roll or a clean tea towel to absorb as much excess water as possible.

Soak the seeds for at least two hours in water, then drain and rinse. Julienne the courgettes, and finely chop the parsley, celery and tomato.

Mix with the remaining ingredients in a large bowl and decorate with courgette shavings and goji berries. Serve with that ecstatic look of yours. I've seen it on you before so don't try to hide it.

savoury snacks and sides

I love having little tubs of stuff in my fridge, so we can go and pick something exciting any time of the day. If you spend a few minutes a day making something that lasts for a week, then there's always a lot of variety to get excited about other than your normal daily diet of fresh salad, smoothies and juices.

Nori batty

- 1 nori sheet
- ½ avocado
- 4 cherry tomatoes
- 5g Engevita
- ½ teaspoon soya lecithin
- ½ teaspoon powdered green superfood
- ½ teaspoon minced parsley

My childhood memories are full of bread and dripping and The Last Of The Summer Wine on the telly. Here's to Evie's memories being slightly different. Serves one. Keeps for one day when refrigerated in a sealed container.

Blend the avocado with the Engevita, lecithin and superfood.

Chop the tomatoes and mix in with the parsley.

Cut the nori into two sheets. Spread the mixture along the length of each sheet, and then roll lengthways. Cut each roll into two pieces and serve.

Soya lecithin contains high amounts of choline. It's impossible to get the RDA of choline from raw plant foods, so it's essential to supplement your growing child.

Kelp contains the essential mineral iodine which regulates thyroid function. It's rare in vegan foods, so you need to make an effort to add kelp to your child's diet every now and then.

- 1 nori sheet
- ½ avocado
- 1 small carrot
- 1 pinch of kelp powder
- 5g golden flax seeds

This is a lovely food for those starting out in the world of tastes. Serves one. Keeps for one day when refrigerated in a sealed container.

Grind the flax to a powder. Blend all the ingredients except for the nori sheet into a paté. Spread the paté all over one side of the nori sheet.

Roll the nori sheet, and seal the open end with water. Using scissors, cut a small part of the end off as there won't be enough paté in there.

Cut the rest of the nori into 2cm pieces. As you cut one end the scissors will cause it to close, and the other end will open like a rose. Arrange in a small dish and serve.

cucumber canapés

Little nibbles for little nibblers. Makes about twelve canapés. Keeps for two days when refrigerated in a sealed container.

½ cucumber
4 tomatoes
20g olives
10g basil

Cut the ends off the cucumber and cut into rounds, about 5mm thick. Lay them out on a plate.

Blend the remaining ingredients, but keep some texture in it. Place about a heaped teaspoon of the mixture on each cucumber round. If you're feeling fancy, top it off with a basil leaf and half an olive.

This is a great favourite of Evie's. Parsley is a great source of iron: just two sprigs a day provide a small child with their RDA. Serve this with a small glass of orange juice, as the vitamin C helps with iron absorption. Serves one. Keeps for one day when refrigerated in a sealed container.

1 nori sheet
2 sprigs of flat leaf parsley
½ avocado
5g Seagreens
1 small tomato

Finely chop the parsley and tomato. Mash with the avocado and Seagreens.

Using scissors, cut the nori into four squares. Spread a quarter of the mixture onto each square, and roll it up to make a sausage shape.

You can serve them like this to bigger children. For toddlers, cut the sausages up into inch wide "parcels".

veggie chips

- 2 tomatoes
- 2 celery stalks
- 4 carrots
- 4 broccoli florets
- 1 red or orange pepper
- 10g parsley
- 5g kelp powder

Looks like bark, but actually tastes quite nice. Evie likes to dip these. Makes about 40 chips, depending on size. Keeps for about two weeks when stored in a sealed container.

Remove the seeds and stalk from the pepper. Blend everything together in a high-speed blender.

Pour the liquid onto a lined dehydrator tray, and spread until it's about 8mm thick.

Dehydrate at 115°F/46°C for about eight hours. The sheet may wrinkle up a bit. Peel the one large veggie chip from it, and break up into appropriate sizes.

crisps

2kg sweet potatoes
20ml raw sesame oil
5g Himalayan pink salt

This is one of Evie's favourite snacks. Sweet potatoes are very filling and tasty, and much more nutritious than ordinary white potatoes. However, if you can find organic heirloom potatoes that aren't floury, then give those a go to ring the changes. Makes about ten portions, depending on size. Keeps for about four weeks when stored in a sealed container.

Cut the potatoes into quarters, or a size that will work with your food processor. Using the slicer attachment on your food processor, chip all the potatoes. You may need to do this in two batches. When all the potatoes are chipped, put them into a large mixing bowl. Fill this bowl with water and swish it around for about five minutes. The water will turn orange, and a good deal of starch will come out. Drain the potatoes, mopping up any excess water on them with a kitchen towel.

Add the oil and salt to the bowl of chips and mix well with your hands. Place these coated potatoes onto dehydrator sheets, unlined. Spread them thinly, but it doesn't matter if they're touching as they'll curl away from each other in the drying process. Dehydrate at 115°F/46°C for 18 hours, or until crispy.

When ready, they will crunch like crisps in your mouth. If they're still chewy, dehydrate them for a little longer.

Kate's crackers

- 1 litre water
- 250g golden flax seeds
- 60g shelled hemp seeds
- 60g sesame seeds
- 60g pumpkin seeds
- 50g Clearspring's Atlantic sea salad
- 20ml tamari
- 10g purple corn extract

Yes she is. So I asked her to contribute a recipe of said name. I think in her next life she'll be very sane and boring, but I doubt a recipe called Kate's sane and boring would be very tasty. Here's Kate Magic:

We don't eat many nuts in our house apart from almonds because they're full of calcium, and brazils for the selenium. We eat lots of seeds, though, especially flax and hemp. I feel they're two of the very best foods for growing little brains and bodies big and strong. These crackers are Xseedingly good. Time needed: 12 hours presoaking and 18 hours dehydrating. Makes about 60 crackers. Keep for a couple of months in an airtight container.

Soak the flax seeds in 750ml of the water overnight, or for at least eight hours. Give them a swish around in the water with your hands: I like to knead them a bit to ensure all the water is evenly absorbed.

When soaked, add remaining ingredients. Give it a really good mix with a spoon to make sure everything is well distributed. Soak for another four to eight hours.

Spread over three dehydrator trays lined with sheets. Dehydrate at 115°F/46°C for twelve hours, then score and flip onto unlined trays and dry another six hours.

crackers indian style

1 large cauliflower
5 medium carrots
120g sunflower seeds or almonds
60g golden flax seeds
½ leek
10g cumin seeds
10g coriander seeds
10g fresh coriander leaves
1 teaspoon paprika
½ teaspoon turmeric
2 cloves of garlic
½ inch of ginger

OK, so I admit I'm not very good at making crackers. This is a recipe lovingly donated by my soul sister Jatinder; I've adapted it a bit for very small children. Jatinder lives in Spain with her three raw children and husband Derek. Born and raised in India, she had spices in much of her childhood food. Spices are great for keeping baddies out of the body, and they contain essential trace elements, too. Here's Jatinder:

This is a versatile little recipe. Instead of crackers, you could make these into balls or slightly thicker but less spicy for toddlers so their mouths and little hands can handle them. You could count with them as they munch their way through! What a great way to learn to count!

In a food processor, process the cauliflower, carrots, leek, garlic and ginger until you have very fine kibbles.

Add the sunflower seeds or almonds and flax seeds to the dry jug of your high-speed blender and make a flour.

Crush the cumin and coriander seeds in a pestle and mortar, or use a spice mill if you have one.

Finely chop the coriander leaves.

Place all above ingredients in a large mixing bowl and knead until you have an even dough. Leave for five minutes. Spread 5mm thin onto lined dehydrator trays. Dehydrate at 115°F/46°C for four hours, flip, remove sheets and dehydrate for a further four hours or until crisp.

Big potatno cake

400g parsnips
200g cauliflower
175ml olive oil
50g cashew nuts
6 dates
Pinch of unrefined sea salt

Exactly. It has no potatoes in it but kind of tastes like it has, so it's potatno. No-one can believe what's (not) in it because it tastes so much better than the ingredients suggest. Makes eight portions. Keeps for three days when refrigerated in a sealed container.

Soak the cashew nuts in water for thirty minutes, then drain and rinse. Top and tail the parsnips and cut them into chunks. Cut the cauliflower into chunks. Add all the ingredients to your food processor and process until everything has been reduced to crumbs.

Transfer this mixture to a jug and use your hand blender to blend to a smooth paste. Put the mixture in a loose-bottomed cake tin and smooth it down. Refrigerate for at least an hour before use. When ready to eat, remove it from the tin by placing it on a plate upside down and pushing the bottom through. Cut as you would a cake and serve with your favourite salads.

Sandwich bread

Try doubling up this recipe if you have a large family to feed. Makes twelve big slices. Keeps for seven days when refrigerated in a sealed container. If the slices become soggy over the days you can freshen them up in your dehydrator for a few minutes before serving.

500g golden flax seeds
200g celery
6 sundried tomatoes
1 yellow pepper seeded
1 clove of garlic
1 medium tomato
1 medium onion
1 small bunch of coriander
5g kelp powder
5g Brazilian ginseng
5g unrefined sea salt

Soak the sundried tomatoes for at least an hour. Remove the seeds and stalk from the pepper. Grind the flax seeds in a high-speed blender to make a flour. Turn it into a large mixing bowl. Add the Brazilian ginseng, salt and kelp to this bowl.

In your high-speed blender, add all the remaining ingredients and blend until very smooth. Pour this mixture into the bowl of dry ingredients. Mix it all up using your hands until smooth and even.

Divide the mixture into two and put each half on a lined dehydrator tray. Spread the mixture out right to the edges and make sure it's as even as possible. Dehydrate at 115°F/46°C for four hours. By this time the "bread" should be firm, flexible and not sticky in the middle. If it's sticky, dehydrate for a while longer.

Turn the bread over so the dehydrator liner is on top, and then gently peel the liner off. Dehydrate for a further hour. You can then remove the bread and cut each one into six slices (for large-sized bread) or twelve (for small bread).

Carrot Wraps

1kg carrots
300g golden flax seeds
5g paprika
Large pinch of Himalayan pink salt

Here's something to stuff full of nice things like sprouts and guacamole. Makes eight wraps. Keeps for seven days when refrigerated in a sealed container.

Grind the seeds to a powder using a high-powered blender and its dry jug. Using the wet jug of your powerful blender, purée the carrots.

Divide into two equal halves and spread each half on a dehydrator tray lined with a sheet. Dehydrate for four hours at 115°F/46°C. Turn them over, remove the sheets, and dehydrate for one more hour. Cut into quarters. They are now ready to use or store once cooled.

Variation: To make carrot crackers, alter the one hour of drying time to ten further hours (or overnight), then cut or break into crackers. When completely dry, these will store for about two months in a sealed container.

Not Kate's tomato crisps

My bezzie mate Kate invented the original recipe for this, and it's been heavily borrowed by braw foodists the world over. A braw is someone who brags that they are raw, missing the point that raw foodism should make you more humble. This is my version of Kate's classic. Ideal when you have more tomatoes than tummy space, and they're on the verge of going too far. Makes about twenty crispy crunchy wafer thin crackers. Keeps for a month when stored in a sealed container.

200g ripe tomatoes
4 sundried tomatoes
10g fresh chives, or half the quantity of dried chives

Soak the sundried tomatoes in water for at least an hour. Blend all the ingredients in a high-speed blender until smooth. Spread the mixture out thinly onto lined dehydrator trays. Dehydrate at 115°F/46°C for about six hours, until crisp. Break into bite-sized pieces. As well as being a great snack, they're a wonderful topping for soups and salads.

Add to any salad for that ploughman's vibe. Makes one large jar. Keeps for seven days when refrigerated in a sealed container.

20g dried apricots
20g dried pineapple
20g dried figs
20g dried raisins
Juice of 2 apples
1cm ginger root
½ teaspoon mixed spice
½ teaspoon ground cinnamon

Put all the ingredients in a bowl and leave for one to two hours to allow the fruit to soak up the juice. Once the juice is soaked, add everything to the food processor and pulse chop until you have a chunky chutney.

My Christmas menifestations

christmas Veggies

I've heard that Jesus likes it when people celebrate his birthday with this recipe and a nut loaf rather than turkey and sausages. Serves four as a side dish. Keeps for three days when refrigerated in a sealed container.

100g carrots
100g broccoli
100g Brussels sprouts
20ml olive oil
Juice of 1 lemon
Pinch of Himalayan pink salt

Thinly slice the sprouts, julienne the carrots, and make small florets out of the broccoli. Add all the ingredients to a wide-bottomed bowl and marinate it overnight.

In the morning, put the bowl in the dehydrator and dehydrate for four to eight hours at 115°F/46°C.

Breadsticks

The holdability factor and the novel shape mean these don't last very long in our house. You can make breadsticks from all of my bread recipes if you blend the mixture enough to prevent it clogging up the piping bag. Also, try different piping bag nozzles for different effects. Makes about twenty sticks, depending on length. Keeps for seven days when refrigerated in a sealed container.

200g golden flax seeds
100g raw macadamia nuts
100g goji berries
6 pears
4 sundried tomatoes
5g Brazilian ginseng powder
1 teaspoon barley miso

Soak the sundried tomatoes in water for at least an hour. Soak the goji berries for about five minutes just to soften. Discard the soak waters.

Grind the flax seeds with the macadamia nuts to a flour and add to a large mixing bowl. Core the pears, and discard the cores. Blend the pears with the goji berries, miso and tomatoes until smooth. Add this mixture and the Brazilian ginseng to the mixing bowl. Mix well by hand until even.

Put the mixture into a piping bag with the nozzle of your choice (not too thin). Pipe the sticks onto lined dehydrator sheets. Place in a dehydrator and dehydrate at 115°F/46°C for at least eight hours, maybe twelve, depending on the thickness of your sticks.

Med bread

When Evie first had this she said, "Wow, that's amazing." Since then I make double the quantity. This is great with a miso dip or served with soups. Makes one loaf. Keeps for seven days when refrigerated in a sealed container.

200g green olives, stoned
200g pumpkin seeds ground
50g golden flax seeds
50g tomatoes
40ml olive oil
20g pine nuts
20ml water
20g basil leaves
1 pepper
1 spring onion
1 teaspoon pizza herbs
Large pinch of Himalayan pink salt

Grind the flax and pumpkin seeds to a fine powder using a high-powered blender and its dry jug. Add this to a large mixing bowl.

Blend the olives with the water until smooth. Roughly chop the spring onion. Seed the pepper and quarter it. Add the tomatoes, pizza herbs, olive oil, salt, basil and spring onion to the olives and briefly blend to chop everything finely. Do not over-process as these ingredients are supposed to be chunky.

Turn this mixture out into the seed powder and add the pine nuts before mixing well. Turn this out onto a lined dehydrator tray and mould into a loaf shape, no higher than 3cm. Dehydrate at 115°F/46°C for 24 hours, until soft but not moist inside.

Salba bread

300g golden flax seeds
150g celery
100g Salba or chia seeds
100g tomatoes
100g almonds
50g buckwheaties
50g basil
½ red pepper
2 sundried tomatoes

Salba is a very exciting seed, very similar to chia. Its nutritional values surpass that of any other seed. It has eight times more omega three than salmon. Two days before being introduced to this, I took part in an ayahuasca ceremony and kept seeing fish on trees. I wondered what it meant, then Salba came into my life! Makes one loaf. Keeps for ten days when stored in a sealed container.

Grind the flax seeds to a flour using a high-powered blender and its dry jug. Add all the remaining ingredients to the blender's wet jug, then put the flour in from the dry jug. Blend this until smooth.

Turn out onto a lined dehydrator sheet and form a loaf or small rolls. Dehydrate at 115°F/46°C for four hours before removing the lining, and flipping them. Dehydrate for a further four hours or until firm in the middle, but not hard.

SeaSeeds

Little ones love to munch on crunchy seeds, rammed with nutrition. These great nibbles are easy to put in a packed lunch, and handy between meal times. This recipe takes a few days to prepare, but the tasty results keep for at least six months when stored in a sealed container.

100g sunflower seeds
100g pumpkin seeds
10g Seagreens
20ml hemp sauce
1 lemon

The seeds need to be soaked and sprouted first. Soak all the seeds in water overnight, then in the morning rinse and drain them and leave to rest for a few hours. Rinse them again that afternoon, and then at night. The following morning rinse and drain the seeds one last time.

Sprinkle on the Seagreens and hemp sauce. Thinly slice the lemon and mix the slices into the seeds. Remove any loose lemon pips.

Spread the mixture onto lined dehydrator trays. Dehydrate at 115°F/46°C for 12-18 hours.

Dinosaur caviar

- 1 cucumber
- 10g soft seaweed, such as Japanese sea vegetables or wakame
- 1 black bell pepper (red will do if you can't find black)
- 50g pumpkin seeds, soaked for 1-12 hours
- 20g Peruvian olives, stoned
- 1 level teaspoon Blue Manna powder
- 1 teaspoon dulse powder
- 1 dessertspoon pumpkin oil
- Pinch of Himalayan salt

Great party food, full of stuff that children shouldn't like but somehow they do. Makes about twenty dinosaurs. Keeps for two days when refrigerated in a sealed container.

Soak the seaweed for the required amount of time. Soak the pumpkin seeds for at least an hour, then drain and rinse. Cut the cucumber on the bias (slightly diagonal) into 5mm slices and arrange on a plate.

Reserving some of the pumpkin seeds for decoration, blend all the remaining ingredients to make a chunky relish texture. If it's too thick, add some of the seaweed soakwater. Place one teaspoon on each piece of cucumber. Add the pumpkin seeds to make a spiny back for the dinosaurs and serve.

Olive and sundried tomato focaccia

So tasty and shockingly like the real thing. We double this recipe when we make it, and sometimes we add a twist by swirling raw vegan pesto through it. You can also vary this recipe by adding other herbs inside and on top of the focaccia. Makes one loaf. Keeps for seven days when refrigerated in a sealed container.

250g golden flax seeds
50g green olives, stoned
10ml water
4 sundried tomatoes
5 Peruvian olives
Pinch of sea salt

Soak the sundried tomatoes in water for at least an hour. Add the flax seeds, green olives and water to a high-speed blender. Blend until smooth and creamy. Turn the mixture out onto a lined dehydrator tray and form into a 2cm high bread of any shape (square, round or rectangle, for example).

Chop the sundried tomatoes and Peruvian olives into fine pieces and scatter these over the top of the bread, pushing them in. Sprinkle the salt on top. Dehydrate at 115°F/46°C until it's not sticky in the middle.

Hard cheeze

300g raw cashew nuts
100g coconut butter
1 capsule Blue Manna
50g white miso
¼ teaspoon Himalayan pink salt

This has a real proper cheesy taste and texture. Everyone loves it. Makes one big tub of cheeze. Keeps for two weeks when refrigerated in a sealed container.

Gently melt the coconut butter over a very low flame. Add all the ingredients to a high-speed blender and blend to a very smooth cream. Pour into a mould and refrigerate until hard. Once hard, you can slice and grate it like dairy cheese.

Dips, dressings, sauces and spreads

The best thing about these dishes is that you can add quite large quantities of ecstatic foods to them without the fussy ones noticing. This makes your heart glow, as you know your little ones are getting thoroughly nourished while scoffing their faces.

My mate

40g raw coconut butter
50g raw cashew nuts
15g dark unpasteurised miso
Juice of 1 lemon

This thick and smooth spread tastes just like those yeast extracts but it's much milder so you can use more of it. The miso has to be the darkest you can find to get that flavour. Keeps for up to four weeks when refrigerated in a sealed container.

Soak the nuts for around twenty minutes. Gently melt the coconut butter at a low temperature. Strain the nuts and discard the soak water.

Add all ingredients to a high-speed blender and blend until very smooth. Pour into a tub or dish and leave to set for a few hours in the fridge before using.

cranberry sauce

4 pears
150g dried cranberries
4 apricots

This is great for adding a Christmassy taste to any raw meal. It can also be used as a jam. This recipe gives us the detoxing and protecting powers of cranberries in a sweet, easy to eat sauce. Keeps for seven days when refrigerated in a sealed container.

Soak the cranberries and apricots in water for at least one hour, then drain. Core the pears and roughly chop them. Add all the ingredients to a high-speed blender or hand blender jug and blend until smooth.

Olive and hemp paté

This goes really well with crudités such as red pepper, carrot and fennel. Serves four to six as a spread or dip. Keeps for four days when refrigerated in a sealed container.

100g green olives, pitted
100g shelled hemp seeds
50ml raw sesame oil
10g parsley
½ red pepper
Juice of ½ lime
5g basil leaves
5g hemp leaf powder or green superfood powder
5g sprouted broccoli powder

Make sure all the olives are free of stones, even if you bought stoned ones. You don't want to break your blender or child's teeth on them! Remove seeds and stalk from the pepper.

Add all the ingredients to a high-speed blender or hand blender and blend until smooth. Turn out and garnish with parsley and some diced pepper.

Heaven is a half piped cheezy cucumber

- 100g macadamia nuts
- 1 orange pepper
- 1 tomato
- 1 clove of garlic
- 1 spring onion
- 1 dessertspoon miso
- 1 teaspoon paprika

This cheezy spread has the best consistency for piping onto food and using as canapés for special occasions (that will be every day, then). You could just spread it if you don't want to be a fancy pants. Keeps for around four days when refrigerated in a sealed container.

Remove the seeds and stalk from the pepper. Add everything to a high-speed blender and blend until smooth.

Put the cheeze inside a nozzled piping bag and place in the fridge for ten minutes. Once cooled, pipe onto your desired base and serve. If not eaten immediately, it will store in the piping bag in the fridge.

Rochelle's rockstar cheeze

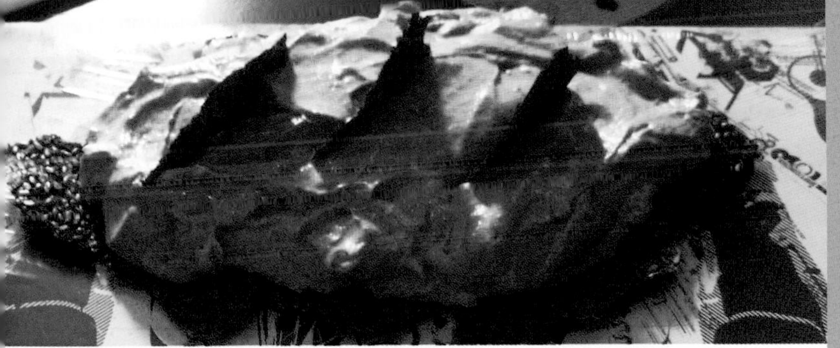

Rochelle's records are the least cheezy out there, so she has to make up for it by eating cheezy food instead. Fermented foods have really special qualities that children love. Celtic sea salt is the tastiest salt option for this recipe — just make sure it's unrefined. Keeps for about seven days when refrigerated in a sealed container.

This is your **Basic cheeze hit**
- 250g raw cashew nuts
- 200-250ml water — depending on how creamy you like the cheese
- 7g Celtic sea salt

Add these for **Fancy cheeze hit**
- ⅓ lemon
- 15g Engevita

Add these as well for **Mountain cheeze hit**
- 30g chia or Salba seeds
- 10g Brazilian ginseng
- 5g lion's mane and/or reishi powder

Optional extras
- ½ clove of garlic
- Crystal energy
- Medicinal mushrooms
- Purple corn extract
- Indian or Italian herbs and spices
- Paprika
- Caraway seeds
- Reiki Symbol 1 if you use Reiki in this way

Soak the nuts in water for about 20 minutes. Discard the water. Remove the skin and pips of the lemon. Add everything to your high-speed blender and blend until smooth. If adding chia or Salba seeds mix them in by hand at the end, after blending.

Pour the mixture into a shallow non-plastic dish. Cover with a clean tea towel or muslin fabric and place somewhere dark for eight to twelve hours. It will develop a deeper, cheezier taste the longer you leave it. Once it tastes good to you, serve or refrigerate to store.

Deeply dippy

A simple yet very moreish dip. The white miso rounds out all the other flavours. Keeps for three days when refrigerated in a sealed container.

- ½ avocado
- 20ml water
- 15g white miso
- 10ml tamari
- ¼ sheet of nori

Crumble the nori. Blend everything until super smooth in a high-speed blender or hand blender.

smooth almond dressing

100ml fresh orange juice
40g raw almond butter
1 teaspoon freshly grated lemon rind
5ml apple cider vinegar

Almonds aren't as acidic as other nuts. They are nourishing and soothing, and provide lots of calcium. Keeps for about three days when refrigerated in a sealed container.

Blend all of these ingredients in a high-speed blender until very creamy. Serve it over shredded lettuce or other crisp salad ingredients.

sweet banana dressing

30g raw tahini
1 banana
1 level teaspoon paprika (optional)

Children love the idea of dressings as they present the opportunity to make a big mess. This is a great dressing for very small ones: it's simple and has that familiar creamy booboo taste. Tahini is extremely high in calcium and should be part of every raw vegan child's daily diet. Keeps for two days when refrigerated in a sealed container.

Add all the ingredients to a high-speed blender and blend until creamy. If it's too thick for your requirements you can thin it down with cucumber, carrot or celery juice.

Pour this over shredded lettuce and mix well before serving. It can also just be eaten on its own as a pudding.

Hempesto

This is a really flavoursome pesto that kiddies seem to love mixed in with mild leaves. Keeps for three days when refrigerated in a sealed container. If you cover the top of it with oil, you'll extend its shelf life.

50g basil
50g parsley
70g raw pine nuts
70g shelled hemp seeds
70g raw macadamia nuts
50ml olive oil
50ml raw hempseed oil
5g Himalayan pink salt
1 small clove of garlic

Add everything except the oils to a food processor or high-speed blender and combine until almost smooth. Add the oils and blend for about five seconds more before serving. Don't over-blend the oils.

Light and fruity, this sauce is perfect for summer days. I add black pepper to mine, but Evie insists she's too young for all that. Keeps for up to three days when refrigerated in a sealed container.

3 medium tomatoes
2 courgettes
1 small leek
1 heaped teaspoon raw vegan pesto
Pinch of Himalayan salt

Top and tail the courgettes and leek. Add everything to a high-speed blender and blend until nearly smooth. Feel free to top with another dollop of pesto before serving — we do!

Cottage Squeeze

- 50g pumpkin seeds
- 50g sunflower seeds
- 50g cashew nuts
- 50g macadamia nuts
- 20g coriander
- 10g hemp sauce
- 10ml water
- 20ml raw apple cider vinegar
- 30ml Udo's Choice oil
- 1 apple
- ½ lemon, including rind
- 3 raw cacao beans
- Pinch of Himalayan salt

This reminds me of my mum in the 80s, always on a diet eating cottage cheese on rye crackers. Evie's mum thankfully found a way out of the diet trap and she thanks her lucky thighs every day. Keeps for up to four days when refrigerated in a sealed container.

Soak the seeds and cashew nuts for at least one hour in water. Rinse, drain and then discard the water.

Put all the ingredients in a high-speed blender or food processor and blend until creamy but not totally smooth.

Sauces for courses

Deeper and darker than the salsa, this sauce is great as a topping and also makes a wonderful "pasta" sauce when served with spiralised courgette or squash. Keeps for about four days when refrigerated in a sealed container.

Soak the sundried tomatoes for about an hour, then drain. Add all the ingredients to a high-power blender and blend until smooth.

50g red pepper
20g sundried tomatoes
20g coriander leaves
20ml olive oil
20ml water
5ml tamari

Hempshine dip

100g sunflower seeds
20g parsley
20g shelled hemp seeds
40ml olive oil

Texture is everything in this dish. Keep the blending light — just enough to cream everything together. Sprouted sunflower seeds are fourth-dimensional foods and full of extra energetic loveliness. Keeps for about three days when refrigerated in a sealed container.

Soak the sunflower seeds in water overnight. Rinse and strain, then allow to sprout for two days, rinsing and straining every twelve hours.

Once the seeds are sprouted blend all ingredients in a high-speed blender, keeping some texture.

Salbamole

2 avocados
10g Salba or chia seeds
10g white miso
10g raw coconut butter
10g Seagreens
10g raw cashew nuts
5g coriander-flavoured raw vegan pesto

High in omegas and calcium, this dip or spread is a delight. Keeps for two days when refrigerated in a sealed container. If you want to extend its shelf life, add some lemon juice and ionic silver.

Peel and stone the avocados. Put everything in a food processor or high-speed blender and blend until smooth and creamy.

Hummous cheeze

200g tahini
200g almonds
100g green olives, stoned
50ml olive oil
Juice of 1 lemon
2 cloves of garlic
1 medium tomato
2 sundried tomatoes
¼ teaspoon ground black pepper
¼ teaspoon Himalayan pink salt

This is a soft cheese with a Mediterranean feel. It can also be used as a dip if you add more water or juice. Try not to break too many plates when making this, but feel free to pin five pound notes onto your child's frock. Keeps for around seven days when refrigerated in a sealed container.

Soak the sundried tomatoes and almonds in water for at least an hour, then drain and rinse. Check the olives for stray stones.

Add all the ingredients except the olive oil to a high-speed blender or food processor, putting the watery ingredients in the bottom and the nuts in the top. Blend everything until nearly smooth.

Put the blender on slow and gradually pour in the oil until it's well-blended. Turn out into a tub and pat down well to compress it. Refrigerate for a couple of hours and then scoop out or turn the whole semi-soft "cheeze" out and slice it.

Evie can't believe it's not goat's cheese paté

80g soaked pumpkin seeds
30ml water
10g white miso
10g hemp seed butter
5g dried shiitake mushrooms
5g spring onion greens
1 large portobello mushroom

By this point you may be thinking: "How many cheezes do you think we need, Shazzie?" But I promise you, these are so well-loved by children and so nutrient-dense that you need to know about all of themmm. Keeps for about four days when refrigerated in a sealed container.

Soak the pumpkin seeds and shiitake mushrooms in water for at least an hour. Rinse them, drain and discard the water. Peel the portobello mushroom and remove the stalk. Put all the ingredients in a high-speed blender and blend until smooth.

creamy curry dressing

Evie adores this dressing. When she's big she'll eat whole chillis just like her Grandma. When she was two she found some dried chillis and rubbed them all over her face. Maybe she'll never be like Grandma after all. Keeps for three days when refrigerated in a sealed container. You can extend the shelf life to seven days by adding a dessertspoon of ionic silver.

Core the apple. Add everything to a high-powered blender and blend until smooth.

- 50g raw pine nuts
- 50ml raw pumpkin oil
- 50ml water
- 30g raisins
- ½ apple
- ½ banana
- Juice of 1 orange
- 1 clove of garlic
- 1 level teaspoon mild curry powder
- 1 spring onion
- Pinch of Himalayan pink salt

summer salsa

1 small courgette
85g vine tomatoes
10g raw vegan pesto
5ml raw pumpkin seed oil
¼ clove of garlic

Great for picnics, this salsa blobs itself nicely onto the top of all crackers, breads and burritos. Evie loves hers with baby sweetcorn on the side. Actually, she loves everything with baby sweetcorn on the side. Keeps for around four days when refrigerated in a sealed container.

Crush the garlic. Blend everything in a high-power blender or food processor until smooth yet still textured.

All children love sweet flavours, and raw children are lucky to get sweets so healthy they're allowed to have no main course!

Spoilt for chocolate cake

To make the base
160g raw cacao butter
90g Incan berries
70g raw mesquite powder
60g raisins
60g raw almonds
60g lúcuma powder
60g raw cacao powder
40g raw walnuts
5g Brazilian ginseng

To make the topping
100g raw cacao butter
50g raw coconut butter
40g raw cacao powder
60g raw mesquite powder
10g purple corn extract
Pinch of Himalayan pink salt

Too much chocolate will spoil you in the end, and then you'll never settle for anything less. Makes eight generous slices. Keeps for up to three weeks in a sealed container in the fridge.

Base: Gently melt the cacao butter at a low temperature. In a food processor, crumble the fruit and nuts. In a large mixing bowl, mix all ingredients together. Press into a loose-bottomed cake tin and refrigerate.

Topping: Gently melt the cacao and coconut butters at a low temperature. Add all ingredients to a mixing bowl and whip together to form a cream. Spread this cream evenly over the base, and return to the fridge to set for at least thirty minutes before cutting and serving.

shoelaces

Before a child can learn to tie her shoelaces, it's important for her to eat them. Makes about twenty laces. Keeps for over six months when refrigerated in a sealed container.

1 medium and very ripe mango
1 sweet pear
1 ripe banana

Peel and stone the mango. Peel the banana. Core the pear. Cut the ingredients into chunks and blend in a high-speed blender until liquified. Pour the liquid onto a dehydrator tray topped with a sheet and dehydrate for about eight hours at 115°F/46°C. When dry, peel away from the sheet and cut into thin strips.

Evie's Oompa Loompa cake

250g raisins, not soaked
130g raw cacao butter
130g raw cashew nuts
60g raw hemp seed butter
50g raw carob powder
30g crushed cacao nibs
30g raw hemp protein powder
2 teaspoons Crystal Manna
10g maca powder
10ml raw agave nectar
5g purple corn extract
¼ orange, including skin

I made this to make sure Evie was getting a good concentrated source of protein. Add a touch of ginger to get the best ever chocolate ginger cake. Makes about 16 slices. Keeps for seven days when refrigerated in a sealed container.

Gently melt the hemp and cacao butters at a low temperature.

Mix all the ingredients together with a fork, and then put it into a high-speed blender. Blend all the ingredients until smooth. The mixture should just plop out of the blender into a mould. If it doesn't, add other wet or dry ingredients as necessary and blend again.

Spread the mixture evenly in your mould. I add cling film to mine to enable it to turn out easier. Place it in the fridge for at least two hours to set.

Sweet omega pudding

Simple and creamy, little kiddies love this. Serves two. Keeps for three days when refrigerated in a sealed container.

Add everything to a high-speed blender and blend until smooth. Serve in a bowl with extra agave nectar swirled on top. Add berries or dried fruit if desired.

- 200g cantaloupe melon
- 200g shelled raw hemp seeds
- 10ml raw agave nectar
- 20ml Udo's Choice oil
- 5g raw coconut butter
- 5g maca powder
- 5g raw mesquite powder

Purple corn and fig crunchy buns

These may not last too long because they're ridiculously tasty. Makes around twelve buns, depending on case size. Keeps for five days when refrigerated in a sealed container.

Gently melt the cacao butter at a low temperature. Peel and then mash the figs in a mixing bowl. Add all the other ingredients and mix until even. Spoon into little silicone cup cake moulds. Set in the fridge for about an hour before serving.

- 100g raw lúcuma powder
- 70g raw cacao butter
- 3 fresh figs
- 50g buckwheaties
- 5g purple corn extract
- 5 drops of vanilla extract

500g buckwheat
250g pecan nuts
200g shelled hemp seeds
120g raisins
50g mesquite powder
4 softdried figs (or 4 dried figs, soaked in water for 2 hours)
2 bananas
20g raw cacao powder
10g golden flax seeds
10g maca powder

This is a favourite of mine, and so filling. Evie was never so keen but it didn't stop me making them! Though there are lots of ingredients it's a really quick and simple recipe, and I've honestly never tasted a raw brownie that's so succulent and smooth and juicy. Keeps for a week when refrigerated in a sealed container.

Soak the buckwheat in water overnight. Drain and rinse.

Put the figs, bananas, flax seeds, maca and cacao powder into a high-speed blender. Blend everything until it makes a thick batter. Pour this batter into a mixing bowl.

In a food processor, chop the pecans until they're broken into small pieces. Add these and all the other ingredients to the batter. Mix this by hand (do not blend any more).

Pour the mixture onto a dehydrator tray lined with a sheet and form it into a square about 2.5cm high. At this point it should resemble a thick cake. If it's not holding its shape, add more mesquite powder until it does. Cut this into bars or squares and dehydrate for two hours at 115°F/46°C.

After two hours, place a dehydrator tray without a sheet on top of the brownies. Flip the whole lot over, remove the original tray and sheet and carefully separate the brownies on their new tray. Return to the dehydrator for a further two hours at the same temperature.

Love biscuits

Peanuts can contain the carcinogenic substance aflatoxin, which grows on the mould. Obtain organic or wild peanuts and ensure they're mould-free. Makes about forty biscuits. Keeps for a week when refrigerated in a sealed container.

225g raw peanuts
200g raw pecan nuts
120g raw mesquite powder for recipe
40g raw mesquite powder for rolling
100g lúcuma powder
100g purple corn powder
35g maca powder
2 pears, stalks and seeds removed

Remove the stalks and seeds of the pears. Blend the peanuts, pecans and pears in a high-speed blender. Add this to all the other ingredients in a large mixing bowl and mix it all by hand until you have a dough.

Roll the dough until it's 6mm thin, using mesquite powder as a flour to stop it sticking. Cut out the shapes and place on a dehydrator tray. Dehydrate at 115°F/46°C for six to eight hours.

Mango pudding

1 ripe medium mango
50g lúcuma powder
50g raw mesquite powder
10ml raw agave nectar
50g shelled hemp seeds
150ml coconut water
5g raw coconut butter

Evie makes strange whimpering noises whenever I cut a mango. Serves one hungry mummy and a fussy toddler. Keeps for two days when refrigerated in a sealed container.

Peel and stone the mango. Blend everything in a high-speed blender until really smooth and creamy. Serve with love and some hemp seed sprinkles. I like to top this with lecithin for extra choline.

Goji pudding

120g goji berries
70g cashew nuts
40g young coconut jelly (optional)
40g lúcuma powder
25g shelled hemp seeds
10g coconut butter
10g raw cacao butter
5ml lemon juice

So delightful. And red. Children appear to love red food. Serves four. Keeps for three days when refrigerated in a sealed container.

Soak the cashew nuts in water for two hours, then drain and rinse. Gently melt the cacao butter over a low heat. Soak the goji berries in water for five minutes to soften them enough for blending. Drain them from the water (you can use the water in another recipe or drink it as it is).

Add all the ingredients to a high-powered blender and blend until smooth and creamy. Serve in bowls, topped with extra goji berries.

Sunshiney day

A lovely pudding to bring even more light into your life because you can never have too much. Serves two. Keeps for three days when refrigerated in a sealed container.

Peel the banana. Peel and deseed the papaya. Blend everything until very smooth in a high-speed blender. Sprinkle the gold flakes on top and serve in bowls.

- 1 banana
- 1 papaya
- 10g coconut butter
- 20g maca powder
- 5mm slice of ginger
- ½ teaspoon lemon peel
- 1 capsule of digestive enzymes
- 1 capsule of nopal cactus powder
- ⅛ teaspoon etherium gold powder
- Gold flakes to sprinkle when you want to go too far

Eclipse

As above, but add a generous topping of crystal manna so it's dark green when you first see it and then when you dip your spoon a golden flash of light strikes you when you least expect it.

Mix of munch

This is really simple and you can vary the ingredients according to what you can find. Make sure you don't buy dried fruit coated in sugar, oil or honey. If you can't find uncoated fruit you can dry your own with a dehydrator. I often use currants in preference to raisins because they're easier to find without added oil. You can easily put some into a small bag for a lunchbox snack. Keeps for over six months in a sealed container.

Add everything to a large jar, put the lid on and shake to mix.

- 100g dried banana cubes
- 50g raw coconut chips
- 100g dried papaya
- 100g currants
- 100g pumpkin seeds
- 50g goji berries

MeXicoco

Jelly of 1 young coconut
⅛ teaspoon purple corn extract
½ lime
½ teaspoon paprika
¼ teaspoon açai powder
½ teaspoon Himalayan pink salt

David and Evie have a lovely bond. When she was in my tummy David and I went to visit Uri Geller at his house. Uri energised my bump and we had such spoon-bending fun. I bet she remembers meeting the world's most famous psychic before she was born. David's web sites are www.sunfood.com, www.thebestdayever.com and www.ftpf.org.

I once went to Mexico with one of my best friends, the superfood guru David Wolfe. We had these traditional coconut feasts made of jelly coconut, chilli, lime and salt. I loved it so much that I decided to make a child-friendly version.

Scoop the jelly out of the coconut and cut it into 2cm ribbons, then place it in a dish. Mix the powders together and sprinkle onto the coconut meat.

Cut the lime into three chunks, and top the dish with them. Serve, and then squeeze the limes over the dish to eat.

clever mummy sorbet

1 pineapple
3 celery stalks
30ml raw agave nectar
20g raw coconut butter

Clever mummies always find tricky ways to get vegetables into their children. This sorbet is gorgeous, and has lots of celery in it! Makes one tub, keeps for up to three months in the freezer.

Peel, top and bottom the pineapple and cut it into chunks. Add everything to a high-speed blender and blend until liquified.

Pour this liquid into a tub with a lid and freeze. Thaw for five minutes before scooping, and place unused sorbet straight back in the freezer.

Admmm's apple pie

You can make more pies but they are so deep-filled that you will probably have to share each one. Some people have personal trainers; I had Admmm and he was my Personal Jesus until he left his earthly body and became fully expanded bliss and consciousness. Makes two deep pies. Keeps for about a week when refrigerated in a sealed container.

For the base
50g dates
40g raw pecans
35g raw cashew nuts
15g golden flax seeds
10g raw mesquite powder
5ml nut or seed oil

For the filling
2 dessert apples
30g raisins
10ml raw agave nectar
10 pine nuts for garnish
¼ teaspoon cinnamon powder

Core and peel the apples. Blend the flax seeds, cashew nuts, pecans and dates in a high-speed blender until they form a rough dough.

Line two 8cm pastry cases with nut oil and then sprinkle with the mesquite (to stop the base sticking). Divide the base mix into two and press into the cases, covering the bottom and sides evenly.

Blend the apples, raisins and cinnamon until they form a smooth purée and pour this into the lined cases. Swirl some agave nectar over each pie and use the pine nuts to make a small flower shape on each pie.

Dehydrate the pies at 115°F/46°C for eight hours. Then gently turn upside down to release the pies from the tins. Place the pies back onto a dehydrator tray and dehydrate for a further two hours to crisp up the pastry shell before serving.

Revel In Paradise, Admmm.

Ecstacake

500g hemp seeds shelled
250g goji berries soaked
200g lúcuma
75ml soak water
50g golden flax seeds
10g Brazilian ginseng
¼ teaspoon Himalayan pink salt
¼ teaspoon vanilla extract or seeds scraped from ¼ vanilla pod

This makes two cakes, to be sandwiched together. It's nut free, so if you want a nut free topping as well then replace the cashew nuts in Soft chocolate fudge icing **with an equal weight of shelled hemp seeds. I argue with Evie as to who licks the blender with this cake! The cake pictured has a touch of grated raw cacao butter on top. Serves 16. Keeps for about a week when refrigerated in a sealed container.**

Soak the gojis in water for ten minutes, then strain, reserving the soak water. Add the goji berries to a high-speed blender. Add 35ml of the soak water and half of the hemp seeds and blend until smooth.

Grind the flax seeds and add this to a mixing bowl with all the other ingredients. Mix everything together until well combined. Divide into two equal amounts, and place them onto a dehydrator sheet. Mould two equal cake shapes out of the mixture about 3cm thick with your hands. Dehydrate them at 115°F/46°C for twelve hours.

When your cakes are ready, fill and ice with the following recipes. To ice, slowly pour the icing over the top of the cake and use a spatula to move it around the top and coax it down the sides. Then draw the spatula upwards, bringing the icing back up whilst turning the plate. I find that going round the cake three times like this gives a really smooth finish, as the icing sets as I do it.

Refrigerate your finished cake for at least an hour before serving.

Gloopy chocolate dip

100g raw agave nectar
50g raw cacao powder
30g raw coconut butter

Perfect for filling cakes, yet equally welcomed for dipping fruit into. Fills one cake, as above.

Put all ingredients in a small bowl and mix until smooth. Spread on the top of one of the cakes, then sandwich the cake together before icing.

Bloopy chocolate dip

As above but with the contents of one Blue Manna capsule emptied into the bowl before mixing.

soft chocolate fudge icing

This is my cake topping of choice. Makes one cake topping, as above. It also makes a lovely soft fudge if you pour it into a big mould and set it in the fridge, before cutting it up.

100g raw cashew nuts
100g raw cacao butter
50g raw agave nectar
50g raw cacao powder
20g raw coconut butter
1 level teaspoon purple corn extract

Gently melt the cacao butter and coconut butter at a low temperature. Add everything to a high-speed blender or hand blender and blend until smooth. Quickly spread onto the cake before it sets, as directed above.

Pancakes for any Tuesday because they're all special

500ml water
150g raw buckwheat
100g golden flax seeds
100g raw macadamia nuts
20g raw mesquite powder
20g lúcuma powder
20ml raw agave nectar
1 level teaspoon Brazilian ginseng
¼ teaspoon salt

If you're making these for the evening of Pancake Day, start them in the morning and they'll be ready by about 5 or 6pm. Perfect. They're great served with Lemon syrup**, and you can also add soft fruit such as bananas and strawberries. You can even make a nut cream or ice cream and use those as fillers. They make great wraps for any sweet food. Makes eight large pancakes. Will keep for about a week when refrigerated in a sealed container, but are nicer when warmed through in the dehydrator for thirty minutes.**

Soak the buckwheat in water for 20-30 minutes, then discard the water. Grind the flax seeds to make flour.

Pour the water into a high-speed blender. Add the buckwheat and macadamias, and blend until smooth. Add all the other ingredients except the flax flour and blend again until smooth. Finally, add the flax four and blend again. If it goes too stiff, add a little more water. You want a batter that's thicker than normal pancake batter, but still pourable.

Once you have the right consistency, prepare eight dehydrator trays with sheets on top. Pour equal amounts of batter onto each sheet and then whirl the batter round with your fingers until it's about 4mm thick and evenly round. Dehydrate at 115°F/46°C for six hours. Put a new tray without a sheet on top of each pancake, flip the whole lot over and peel the sheets off the pancakes. The pancakes will now be turned and just on trays to allow more air to circulate. Dehydrate for another two hours. By this time, they'll be evenly coloured and can be served warm.

Lemon syrup

This is a delicious little topping for all creams, ice creams and pancakes. Keeps for about two weeks when refrigerated in a sealed container.

50g raw agave nectar
Juice of 1 lemon
1 teaspoon lemon zest
1 teaspoon ground cinnamon

Put all the ingredients into a jar and seal with the lid. Shake the mixture and then pour or store until you're ready to use it.

Dried pear with mulled goji salsa

A simple non-fat recipe for when your small one wants something light. Serves two. Keeps for around four days when refrigerated in a sealed container.

4 dried pears
30g goji berries
5ml raw agave nectar
Pinch of cinnamon powder
Pinch of clove powder
Pinch of nutmeg powder

Soak the goji berries and pears for two hours together in water. Strain, and use the soak water in another recipe, or drink it.

Put 95% of the berries in a high-speed blender with the spices and agave nectar, then blend until smooth. Place the pears in a bowl, pour over the goji sauce, sprinkle on the remaining berries and serve.

Layers of love

Layer 1
170g strawberries

Layer 2
150g strawberries
70g goji berries
50ml soaking water (use in recipe)
30g raw macadamia nuts
20g raw cacao powder
5g purple corn extract

Layer 3
100g raw cashew nuts
100ml soaking water (don't use in recipe)
50g raw macadamia nuts
40g shelled hemp seeds
30ml raw agave nectar
½ teaspoon vanilla extract
10ml water

Layer 4
30g strawberries

This is really light and creamy. It's best served in glass dishes, so you can appreciate its full beauty. Serves two. Keeps for two days when refrigerated in a sealed container.

Soak the goji berries in its soaking water for at least ten minutes, and the nuts in their soaking water for at least an hour. Don't soak the gojis and nuts together as you need to use the water from the berries, and you shouldn't use nut soak water.

Thinly slice the layer 1 strawberries and lay on the base of your dish.

Blend the layer 2 ingredients, including the soak water, into a sauce and pour over the strawberries.

Blend the layer 3 cream in a high-speed blender until smooth and spoon over layer 2.

Finely slice the layer 4 strawberries and lay over the creamy topping.

Refrigerate for at least thirty minutes to allow the cream to stiffen up slightly, giving it an extra luscious texture.

I Scream for more

Raw ice creams are limitless and such fun to make. Here are Evie's favourites. If you have an ice-cream maker, use the same ingredients and method, then add to your machine for a fluffier finish. Keeps in a sealed tub in the freezer for around two weeks.

200g peeled, frozen bananas (freeze for about 24 hours before making this recipe)
60g raw pistachio nuts, shelled
4 dried figs

Soak the pistachios and figs for at least four hours, then drain, discarding the water. Put all ingredients into a high-power blender and blend into a slightly rough cut ice-cream.

Omega dreamy cream

200g peeled, frozen bananas (freeze for about 24 hours before making this recipe)
60g raw cashew nuts
40g shelled hemp seeds
10g lúcuma powder

Full of great-for-your-brain fats, "ice cream brain" takes on a whole new meaning. Keeps in a sealed tub in the freezer for around two weeks.

Soak the cashew nuts for at least four hours, then drain, discarding the water. Put all the ingredients into a high-power blender and blend into smooooth ice cream.

Mount morada

200g peeled, frozen bananas (freeze for about 24 hours before making this recipe)
30g dried pears
30g dried apricots
1 level teaspoon purple corn extract

Children love to make mountains out of molehills. Beat them at their own game by making mountains out of ice cream. Keeps in a sealed tub in the freezer for around two weeks.

Soak the pears and apricots for at least four hours and drain, discarding the water. Put all the ingredients into a high-powered blender and blend until smooth. Serve piled up in a mountain shape.

Flowery apricot fudge

When I cut these into little pieces I wrap them individually in foil and store them in the fridge where Evie can reach. She just helps herself when she fancies a bite. Makes about 40 squares, depending on size. Keeps for about a month when refrigerated in a sealed container.

100g dried apricots
100g raw cashew nuts
100g raw cacao butter
65g raw coconut butter
60g lúcuma powder
20g mesquite powder
5 drops 5% diluted otto rose oil
¼ teaspoon vanilla powder or ¼ teaspoon vanilla essence
⅛ teaspoon etherium pink powder
Pinch of Himalayan pink salt

Gently melt the cacao butter and coconut butter at a low temperature. In a high-speed blender, roughly blend the apricots and cashews. Add all the other ingredients to the blender and blend until smooth.

Pour into a square plastic mould and cool in the fridge. Cut into small pieces when set.

I'm dreaming of a white chocolate

- 140g raw cacao butter
- 140g raw cashew nuts
- 20g raw mesquite powder
- 20ml raw agave nectar
- 5g Brazilian ginseng powder
- 5g Gillian McKeith's Living Food Energy Powder
- 5g maca powder

These are nicest just out of the fridge but are also OK at room temperature. They don't fall apart or melt like the wicked witch or anything. Keep for about a month when refrigerated in a sealed container.

Gently melt the cacao butter over a low flame. Add everything to a high-speed blender and blend until you get a thick liquid. If you don't get a thick "melted chocolate" consistency, then add more of the dry or wet stuff as appropriate.

Pour into moulds of your choice and refrigerate for at least two hours to set. If you're in a hurry, you can freeze for half an hour.

Grandma gives good lolly

- 200ml orange juice, freshly squeezed
- 10ml raw agave nectar
- 3 drops orange oil (optional)

The best thing about going to Grandma and Grandad's house is raiding the greenhouse and the freezer. There are always Evie-mouth-sized delights to be had. Makes about six lollies, depending on mould size. Keeps for about two months when f-f-f-frozen.

Mix everything together, then pour into ice-lolly moulds. Freeze for 4-8 hours before licking.

christine's orchid chocolate

One day Evie's Gran Christine brought us a beautiful orchid, so I just had to make a chocolate to celebrate its presence. Vanilla is the only edible orchid, which is why it's in here. Out of all the chocolates I've made, this one is Evie's favourite as it's light and sweet. Just like her Gran. Chocolate yield depends on size of moulds. Keeps for at least a couple of months in a sealed container in the fridge.

500g raw cacao butter
270g lúcuma powder
100g mesquite powder
60g raw coconut butter
60g raw cacao powder
60g raw agave nectar
½ teaspoon vanilla extract
Pinch of Himalayan pink salt

Gently melt the butters at a low temperature. In a separate bowl, mix all other ingredients together and then pour on the melted butters. Whisk everything, or to make the chocolate super-fine, blend in a high-speed blender for about thirty seconds to a minute. Pour the chocolate into moulds. Allow to set in the fridge before storing or eating. You can pour into one big mould and cut the chocolate up if you don't have enough small moulds.

Golden brown texture like sun

220g goji berries
220g cacao nibs
180g raw cacao butter
2 teaspoons lemon peel

This is the sort of chocolate you take to a party when you want everyone to tell you what a domestic goddess you are. Then you put on an 80s record and dance, while your child pretends she doesn't know you. Makes about twenty chunks, depending on size. Keeps for two weeks when refrigerated in a sealed container.

Gently melt the cacao butter at a low temperature. Add everything to a high-speed blender and blend until smooth.

Pour into a mould of your choice and put in the fridge to set. Some of the lemon peel will float to the top with some cacao butter to give it a special appearance.

Gojiranium Studge

Really, far too moreish for children and adults alike. A finger of studge is just enough to stop you eating your greens. Makes about 40 squares depending on size. Keeps for about a month when refrigerated in a sealed container.

- 100g goji berries, soaked in water for 5 minutes
- 100g cacao butter
- 100g shelled hemp seeds
- 65g coconut butter
- 50g mesquite powder
- 50g maca powder
- 5g Brazilian ginseng
- 5g he shou wu
- 2 drops 100% geranium essential oil
- ¼ teaspoon vanilla powder or ¼ teaspoon vanilla essence
- Pinch of Himalayan pink salt

Soak the gojis in water for five minutes, and discard the water. Gently melt the cacao butter and coconut butter at a low temperature, and add to a large mixing bowl.

Blend the gojis with the hemp seeds and oils, then mix them into the bowl with all the other ingredients.

Pour into a container and set in the fridge.

Purple corn and apricot crumbly chocolate

120g raw almonds
100g raw cacao butter
100g hemp seeds
50g purple corn flour
20g raw cacao powder
20ml raw agave nectar
6 dried apricots
¼ level teaspoon Blue Manna
Pinch of Himalayan salt

This is a fun chocolate to make with your small ones. Sometimes I add some gold flakes on top and tell Evie how precious it is. Then I tell her she's even more precious! Makes about twenty pieces. Keeps for around two months when refrigerated in a sealed container.

Gently melt the cacao butter at a low temperature. Roughly grind the almonds in a food processor. Cut the apricots into strips, using scissors for ease. Add all the ingredients to the cacao butter and mix well. Pour this into a mould or moulds and allow to set in the fridge for a couple of hours.

Home torte

In our home school today, we'll learn how to make the smoothest, creamiest and most delicious torte in the universe. Serves 16 of your children's best friends. Keeps for about a week when refrigerated in a sealed container. Keeps well in the freezer once sliced.

Soak the goji berries in water for five minutes, then discard the water. Gently melt the cacao butter at a low temperature. In a high-speed blender mix all the torte ingredients. Spoon half of the torte mixture into a cake tin and flatten.

Using a hand blender, blend the jam ingredients. Spoon half of this mixture over the already positioned torte mix. Then spoon the remaining cake mix over the jam and the remaining jam over this. Put the cake into a freezer for about an hour to set, but don't freeze it. Alternatively, refrigerate it overnight before slicing.

For the torte
350g strawberries
100g raw cacao powder
100ml orange juice
100g shelled hemp seeds
100g raw cacao butter
60g raw coconut butter
50g goji berries

For the jam
50g strawberries
50g goji berries
50ml orange juice
20g raw agave nectar

Halloween howlers

- 60g raisins or old ladies pupils
- 50g raw cacao butter or bat's droppings
- 50g raw moaning macadamias
- 5g scary purple corn extract
- ½ level teaspoon beastly Blue Manna
- The peel of ¼ orange or some witch's cellulite

Soft and squishy, like a swamp creature's nose. Makes around six howlers, depending on the moulds you can find. Keeps for up to a week in refrigerated in a sealed container.

Spookily melt the cacao butter. Add all ingredients except half the macadamias to a high-speed blender and blend until smooth. Add the rest of the macadamias and blend until they're just crushed. Pour into scary moulds. Set in the fridge for about two hours before turning out and gobbling all up.

smoothies, juices, teas and other drinks

When a child has been loved to life with breastmilk, creating up-to-standard follow-on drinks is quite a challenge! Children love to drink their food! Offer them warm, creamy, light and very smooth drinks. With all of these drinks you can extend the shelf life by adding one teaspoon of ionic silver per 500ml liquid.

incredibly edible chocolate smoovie

400ml water
2 bananas
50g raw cashew nuts
20g raw cacao powder
10g raw carob powder
10ml Udo's Choice oil
5g Gillian McKeith's Living Superfood
5g maca powder

Though I'm not a big banana fan, Evie will enjoy her smoothie to the last drop if she can detect a hint of the bendy yellow fruit. Serves two. Keeps for one day when refrigerated in a sealed container.

Blend everything together using a high-speed blender, then serve.

psychic kale smoothie

100ml water
40g kale
1 large mango
¼ teaspoon purple corn extract
⅛ teaspoon Etherium gold

Purple corn works on the pineal gland, and makes us see beyond the superficialities of Ye Olde 3D Worlde. Serves two. Keeps for one day when refrigerated in a sealed container.

Add everything to a high-speed blender or hand blender and blend until smooth. Strain through a nut mylk bag if your child likes to give you more washing up, then serve.

Auntie Wee Wee

My oldest friend Lisa came to see Evie when she was five days old. Lisa laid her on her knee as she was airing her cho-cho. With divine timing, Evie sprinkled all over Lisa. Then she pulled her own cord off. From that day, the cord has lived in a box in Evie's room and Lisa was renamed Auntie Wee Wee. Serves two. Keeps for three days when refrigerated in a sealed container.

750ml fizzy water
40ml raw agave nectar
40ml fresh lemon juice
5g Brazilian ginseng powder
½ teaspoon lemon peel

Chop the lemon peel into tiny pieces. Add everything except the water to a large jug and blend using a hand-blender. Add the water and stir by hand. To serve, pour into glasses over lots of ice and lemons.

There once was an Auntie called Wee Wee
So called because Evie did pee pee
Whenever she sat
On poor auntie's lap
And all Evie could utter was hee hee!
Love from Auntie Wee Wee

Pink milk

I have this little daughter Evie. She is small and very funny. Evie loves Charlie and Lola and so I made Lola's favourite drink for her. She gets lots of omegas, calcium and other essential-for-growth nutrients in here. Bliss U to Lauren Child for inventing Pink milk. **Serves two, so I put half in the fridge for the next morning. Keeps for one day when refrigerated in a sealed container.**

600ml water
30g Salba or chia seeds
1 small banana
40g raspberries
10ml raw agave nectar
4 Ortho-Bone Vegan capsules
Pinch of Himalayan pink salt

Empty the Ortho-Bone Vegan powder out of the capsules. Add everything to a high-speed blender and blend until the Salba has turned into milk. If you don't blend it for long enough or if your blender's not powerful enough, it won't taste milky. For fussy little ones, strain this through a nut mylk bag.

simply hemp mylk

600ml cold water
100g whole hemp seeds
1 teaspoon raw agave nectar
1 pinch of sea salt

We can all enjoy this as-is, or we grown-ups can pour a dash of it into a warm brew of yerba mate. It's wonderfully versatile and wonderfully good for your little one. Serves two. Keeps for four days when refrigerated in a sealed container.

Soak the hemp seeds for at least six hours. Rinse the seeds and discard the soak water.

Add all the ingredients to a high-speed blender and blend until no more seeds are being pulverised. Strain it thorough a nut-mylk bag or pop sock and then serve.

Omega mylk

1½ litres water
30g raw buckwheat
30g shelled hemp seeds
30g raw pumpkin seeds
30g raw sunflower seeds
30g raw sesame seeds
30g almonds
10g golden flax seeds
30ml raw agave nectar or three dates
⅛ teaspoon Himalayan pink salt

Watching a programme about the state of the nation's health, we saw a family who were all ill and obese. "They haven't got an EFA between them, have they?" piped up Admmm. Let's track them down and give them this mylk to help them out. Serves four. Keeps for three days when refrigerated in a sealed container.

Soak all the nuts and seeds in water for at least eight hours (not the water in the recipe). Strain and rinse, then add to a high-speed blender.

Add all the other ingredients. Blend everything until smooth and creamy. Strain using a nut mylk bag and then strain again using a pop-sock to get the smoothest mylk possible.

Helen's kitchen

Helen makes our kitchen sparkle, and we're really good at messing it up again. She'll never be out of a job, that one. Serves two. Keeps for one day when refrigerated in a sealed container.

250ml water
150g strawberries
80g cashew nuts (soaked for at least 30 minutes)
30g shelled hemp seeds
20ml raw agave nectar
10g raw hemp protein powder
1 celery stalk
2 dried apricots

Soak the cashew nuts for at least thirty minutes, then drain and rinse.

Put all ingredients into a high-speed blender and blend until smooth and creamy.

Mini Doxtor's Juice

1 cucumber
1 bunch of parsley
1 pear
1 head of celery

The skin of cucumbers is high in cholesterol-lowering sterols. This is a great drink to serve to grandparents who have been saving a little extra pudding around their middles for a rainy day.

One day Evie took it upon herself to dress up in my Doxtor's outfit, day-glo footless fishnet tights and all. It should have been wrong, but it somehow looked very very cute. Here's a version of Doxtor's juice that kiddies love. You don't even need a juicer for it. Serves two. Keeps for one day when refrigerated in a sealed container, but best drunk fresh.

Blend all the ingredients in a high-speed blender. Put a nut mylk bag or pop sock over the top of a large jug and pour the mixture in. Squeeze the juice out, or get your small one to do it because it's great fun. Serve and drink immediately.

By the Seaside Smoothie

The celery in this smoothie offers a rounded taste. It's great for feeling like you're swimming in a blue ocean, even if you're stuck in the middle of Cambridge. Serves two. Keeps for one day when refrigerated in a sealed container.

250ml water
3 bananas
2 stalks celery
2 pears
10g green powdered superfood

Peel the bananas and finely chop the celery. It's always best to chop the celery before blending so the strings don't get caught up in the bottom of the blender.

Add everything to a high-speed blender or hand blender and blend until smooth. Strain if your child likes it that way, then serve.

The Princess's Sunshine Smoothie

In my quest to ensure Evie gets her vitamin supplements and herbs, I invented this smoothie. It's so delicious that I can add powders from capsules to my heart's content. Evie has this daily in her Princess cup. I'm surprised she hasn't made a throne out of an old washing up bottle and some sticky backed plastic. Serves two. Keeps for one day when refrigerated in a sealed container.

250ml coconut water
1 banana
20g lúcuma powder
10ml raw agave nectar
10g raw coconut butter
½ teaspoon maca powder

I add to this the contents of: 1 vitamin D2 capsule, 1 reishi mushroom capsule, 1 Brazilian ginseng capsule, 1 Ortho-Bone Vegan capsule.

Peel the banana. Blend everything in a high-speed blender. Serve immediately.

Blade

500ml sparkling water
20ml raw agave nectar
Juice of 1 lemon
1 heaped teaspoon Blue Manna

Blue lemonade. Every child's dream. Well, it was ours when Our Christopher (the official name for my cousin Chris) was about six. We thought Our Auntie Barbara was a magician when she dropped blue food colouring into lemonade and it transformed before our very eyes. Serves two. Keeps for five days when refrigerated in a sealed bottle.

Mix the ingredients in a jug twice the size of the drink (it fizzes up) and pour into tumblers. Easy peasy.

Go juice

Va va voom. Enjoy the day in the fast lane. Not actually literally, that wouldn't be fun for your small one. Serves two. Keeps for one day when refrigerated in a sealed container, but best drunk fresh.

Juice everything and drink immediately. The leftover pulp is great as a base for crackers.

- 50g tomatoes
- 50g carrots
- 50g apples
- 40g spinach
- 40g wild greens or other green leafy vegetables
- 30g cabbage

Goan, Goan, Gone

This is a bit of a meal in a glass. Close your eyes, kick back and pretend you're somewhere else. Serves two. Keeps for one day when refrigerated in a sealed container.

Soak the cashew nuts for at least thirty minutes, then drain and rinse.

Blend all the ingredients in a high-speed blender and blend until smooth. Watch it go!

- 300ml water
- 150g Pakistani mango
- 100g cucumber
- 80g cashew nuts
- 20g lúcuma powder
- 10g coconut butter
- 5 cardamom seeds (scraped from pod)
- Pinch of Himalayan pink salt

A big fat collins

250ml water
10ml raw agave nectar
¼ teaspoon purple corn extract
Juice of ½ lemon

A Collins cocktail for kiddies. Some may say that superfoods are new-fangled and pointless, and suggest children drink sugar-filled blackcurrant drink instead. Not us. All rise for purple corn. Serves two. Keeps for seven days when refrigerated in a sealed container.

Mix the lemon juice, agave nectar and purple corn extract in the bottom of a glass until smooth. Slowly top up with sparkling water, stirring while pouring to allow the goodies to mingle.

I'm NOT tired! tea

"Oh yes you are, you've been up since 5am, it's now nearly midnight and mummy is about to explode. Drink this, love. Now."

10g dried chamomile flower
5g dried lemon balm or 10g if it's fresh
5g dried hops
1 teaspoon raw agave nectar
A mug's worth of boiling water

In a teapot or cafetière steep the herbs in boiling water. Allow to infuse for at least five minutes and pour into a mug or beaker with a little agave nectar. Wait until the tea is cool enough to drink and serve. Lights out!

Invincibili-tea

This is a great drink to gently stimulate the immune system of a poorly little one, or to use every day as a buffer. Evie loves nothing better than a nice cuppotea served in her dolly's tea set.

15g goji berries
5g olive leaves
5g pau d'arco
1 teaspoon raw agave nectar
A mug's worth of boiling water

In a teapot or cafetière steep the herbs in boiling water. Allow to infuse for at least five minutes and pour into a mug or beaker with a little agave nectar. Wait until the tea is cool enough to drink and serve.

Bibliography

Spontaneous Creation — Jock Doubleday

Rainbow Green Live Food Cuisine — Dr Gabriel Cousens

Rewriting the Savage — Julia Douthwaite

Baby Greens — Michaela Lynn

Food for Free — Richard Mabey

Sea Energy Agriculture — Dr Maynard Murray

Nutritional and Physical Degeneration — Dr Weston Price

Biological Transmutations — Louis C Kervran

Optimum Nutrition For Your Child's Mind — Patrick Holford and Deborah Colson

Optimum Nutrition For Your Child — Patrick Holford and Deborah Colson

The Optimum Nutrition Bible — Patrick Holford

The Drinks Are On Me — Veronika Sophia Robinson

Dietitian's Guide to Vegetarian Diets — Virginia & Mark Messina

The Breastfeeding Answer Book — Nancy Mohrbacher & Julie Stock

The Science of Parenting — Professor Margot Sunderland

Unassisted Childbirth — Laura Shanley

The Womanly Art of Breastfeeding — La Leche League

Michele: The Nursing Toddler — Jane Pinczuic

When Breastfeeding Is Not An Option — Peggy Robin

Babywatching — Desmond Morris

Kangarooing Our Little Miracles — Krisanne Larimer

Saying What's Real — Susan Campbell

Flood Your Body with Oxygen — Ed McCabe

DMSO Nature's Healer — Morton Walker

Doctor Yourself — Dr Andrew Saul

Vaccination — Joanna Karpasea Jones

Raising A Vaccine Free Child — Wendy Lydall

The Vaccination Dilemma — Sophia Christine Murphy

The Continuum Concept — Jean Leidloff

Raw Magic — Kate Magic Wood

Spiritual Midwifery — Ina May Gaskin

The Sunfood Diet Success System — David Wolfe

Left In The Dark — Graham Gynn and Tony Wright

The Tipping Point — Malcolm Gladwell

Fast Food Nation — Eric Schlosser

My other books and DVDs

Shazzie's Detox Delights

Detox Your World

Naked Chocolate (with David Wolfe)

Ecstatic Beings (with Kate Magic)

Shazzie's Raw Food Delights

Raw Britannia (free)

Ecstasists Anonymous (free)

I love you so much I give you all this for free

Ecards — save trees, send an ecard from:
shazzie.com/ecards

YouTube — join me at my YouTube channel where I beam directly to you:
youtube.com/valerie1969

Blag — The Doxtor will see you now:
doxtor.wordpress.com

Shazzie Speaks — daily inspiration delivered direct to your inbox:
shazzie.com/products/shazzie_speaks.shtml

Passion magazine — quarterly glossy magazine free to customers:
detoxyourworld.com/acatalog/passion_magazine.html

'Parenting is the journey that makes real adults of us. However much we think we know before we have children, our offspring reveal to us a deeper knowing and a deeper sense of being. Most parents will agree that raising little girls and boys is one of the most challenging, and equally most rewarding, times of their lives. In a culture that values career over family, losing weight over breastfeeding, and making money over spreading love, holistic parenting takes ridiculous amounts of guts, determination, focus and compassion.

So congratulations. If you're holding this book it means you believe it can be done. You believe we can bring our children into a world of love, joy, humour and fulfillment. I believe it too. And I believe this book is going to make it so much easier for so many people. Thank You. And thank you Shazzie.'

— *Kate Magic*